CONVERSATIONS

from the WOMB

CONVERSATIONS
from the WOMB

Communicating with Your Baby
During Pregnancy
and Before Conception

By Penny D. Chang, B.H.S.P., C.M.A.

Healing Heart Press
Charlottesville, Virginia

Healing Heart Press
401 Orange Street
Charlottesville, VA 22902
www.healingheartpress.com

ISBN: 978-0-9857916-0-5
Manufactured in the United States of America

First Edition

Cover Art by Serge Rascle
Cover and Text Design by Zoë Willow
Graphic image *Eternity Turtle* used with permission
from www.tattootribes.com

This book is dedicated to my son, Jacob, who taught me how to talk to babies in the womb, and to all the children yet to be born, whose voices we seek to hear.

Acknowledgements

I would like to thank my husband, Serge, for all his support, patience, encouragement and editing. My heartfelt thanks to all of the following people:

To Joanne Wolf, for her meticulous editing.
To Carol Hurst, for her expert advice and editing.
To Kerry Leavitt, for her helpful guidance on this book and other critical matters.
To Ana Blum, for her energetic support.
To Patricia Phost, who first encouraged the idea of this research.
To Barbara Brennan, and all my teachers and deans at the Barbara Brennan School of Healing, for their teaching and for shepherding the beginning of this research.
To Jane Caplan, who taught me how to finish a book-length manuscript.
To my parents, Martha Miller and Richard Chang, and my brother, Perry Chang, for a lifetime of support and encouragement.
To Judy Steverson, who first taught me how to write.
To my teachers, Jonathan Goldman and Catherine Maguire, for making it possible for me to bring my voice to the world.
To David Chamberlain and Thomas Verny, for their kind encouragement.
To Ursula K. Le Guin, for always inspiring me to seek and name the truth.
To Zoë Willow, for years of encouragement and professional advice.
To all the mothers and children who contributed their voices to the research for this book.

Contents

"But I thought you were forbidden to teach your mind-science to...the natives, until we join the Ekumen."

"Not forbidden. It's not done. I'll do it, though, if you like. And if I can. I'm no Educer."

"There are special teachers of the skill?"

"Yes. Not on Alterra, where there's a high concentration of natural sensitivity, and—they say—mothers mindspeak to their unborn babies. I don't know what the babies answer. But most of us have to be taught, as if it were a foreign language. Or rather as if it were our native language, but learned very late."

Ursula K. Le Guin,
The Left Hand of Darkness

Preface

Connection. How does it begin? The connection between a mother and a child, that most fundamental human bond—when does it start? Most would say it begins at birth, when the new mother sees, hears, and touches her baby for the first time.

But what about before? Few people would deny that a pregnant woman is connected to her baby in some way. What is the nature of that connection? How do we access it? And when does it begin?

This book is about that connection—how it works, when it develops, and how you can access it yourself.

We all know that many women talk to their babies *in utero*, and dream about them during pregnancy. A growing number of books report other kinds of communications between preborn babies and their parents—visions, words, even conversations.

Why do some people have these visions and not others? Are these people only imagining things? Do you have to believe in a certain kind of religious or spiritual framework to develop this connection?

The answer is no. Any parent—or indeed any relative, or perhaps even a close family friend—can develop a strong, conscious connection with a baby-to-be-born. This connection will involve communication at some level. How detailed a response the adult receives to these communications will depend on many factors—the openness of the person involved, the way that person processes information, and how much effort and time she or he spends developing the connection.

In some sense, it matters not at all whether or not you
receive a detailed reply to your side of the conversation. It
also doesn't matter what your outlook on life is, or how your
belief system works. Because I am an energy healer, I see the
world in a certain light. Not everything in this book will ring
true for everyone. I encourage you to take from this book
what works for you, and let go of anything that does not fit
your view of the world.

What matters is that you take the time to communicate
your love to your little one. That, in itself, will be the most
important gift you give your baby, just as your continuing
love and attention will be the most important thing in the
world to your baby after birth, as important as food and
water.

On the other hand, every woman I worked with has been
able to feel some kind of reply or response to her efforts to
consciously connect to her baby. Some women see precise
visual images. Some hear words. Some sense softness, or
feel love. One woman I worked with saw specific colors that
corresponded to the answers to her questions.

Everyone has their own way of receiving communications
from their baby-to-be. You can too. You will—if you want to.
If you practice the exercises in this book—or develop your
own that are more suited to your personality—you will very
shortly find yourself communicating with the baby inside of
you—or the baby you are dreaming about, the one who has
not yet been conceived. Oh yes, you can communicate with
a baby before conception too. Let's take a look at how—and
why.

Chapter One

THE ENERGETIC CONNECTION

It's a sunny morning in May. I wander outside into my back yard. The azaleas are blooming Birds swoop through the tall pine trees. From the woods, a hawk screams.

Spreading a blanket out on the grass, I sit down cross-legged, and place my hands on my swollen belly. I take a few deep breaths, and let myself settle into my body. As I relax, my hands slide to my lap, palms up, my arms forming a circle.

I breathe. Slowly I begin to feel as though my arms are encircling a baby. His head rests in the crook of my left arm. As the feeling grows, I connect with the baby inside of me and ask him what he needs. In response, I hear these words: "Just love me, be with me, spend time with me." I feel the baby smile. "This is nice," he says.

Mothers often talk to their babies during pregnancy. But how many mothers wait for a response? The possibility that I could talk to my baby—and he would respond—would never have occurred to me, had I not been a student at the Barbara Brennan School of Healing during my pregnancy.

In this four-year school of energy healing and self-transformation in Miami, Florida, I learned how each of us is connected to those we love by a set of energetic cords.[1] The cords between us are as real as the hands we hold when we are physically together. They convey emotions, thoughts and intentions, whether we are physically together or not.

We all experience the energetic connection created through these cords, but few of us can name it or describe how it works. Have you ever thought about a friend, only to receive a phone call from that person the very next day? Have you ever known, without being told, that something was wrong with a loved one, many miles away?

In 1995 I was living in Taejeon, South Korea, where I taught English as a Second Language. One night I found myself unable to sleep. My body was stiff; I couldn't relax. I got up in the gray dawn hours, puzzled. What was wrong? I couldn't locate any source for the tension inside my own body. After thinking for a while, I realized that my best friend in my Florida hometown had a baby due that month. I called her house, but received no answer. It took a few days before I learned that the night I couldn't sleep, my friend had gone through a long and strenuous—though ultimately successful—labor and delivery.

This is a perfect example of the energetic connection. My body knew, even though my mind didn't, what my friend was going through, eight thousand miles away. Better put, my energy field knew. Because of my close relationship with my friend, physical distance made no difference. Stress in her body and energy field, conveyed through the energetic cords between us, created an echoing stress in my field and body.

Between children and parents, the energy connection can be even stronger. Some energy cords, Brennan explains, actually

---

[1] Brennan, Barbara, *Light Emerging* (Bantam, 1993), p. 185.

begin to form before conception.[2] (We'll talk more about this in Chapter Three.)

My experimentation with the energetic connection between a mother and her child began in my third year at the Brennan school, when I became pregnant for the first time. As I learned to repair energetic cords on my classmates, I wondered. In cord healings my classmates were experiencing much healing in their relationships with their parents. They even "dialogued" with their parents through those energetic cords, even though their parents were far away, or no longer living. What about the baby I was carrying? Couldn't I use those cords to communicate with him?

I decided to try. Sitting cross-legged on the floor of my living room, I placed my hands on my belly. I sank my hands energetically into my body and tried to make contact with the baby's growing body. Then I tried sensing my baby's energy field. I also tried to feel the cord connecting my baby to my heart. To my surprise and delight, I found that all of these exercises were easy and yielded immediate results.

As I placed my hands on my growing belly, I often felt the baby's energy field as a soft, bright ball of light. I could feel how much bigger his energy field was than his actual physical body. I could also feel how big my energy field had become to adapt to containing both my field and the baby's field.

On several occasions I heard words and responses to questions I asked. My main concern was the baby's health and well being, especially since I had opted not to use ultrasound. Every time I asked, I had a clear sense, and sometimes heard, that everything was all right.

As I developed my communication with my baby, I wondered about other women and their babies. Could

---

[2] Brennan, Barbara, *Light Emerging* (Bantam, 1993), p. 184.

anyone learn to do these exercises? I decided to find out. I developed written exercises based on my experiences and gave them to several women I knew and others who had heard about my project and who were pregnant or who were trying to conceive. I used the results of their experiences to write my senior thesis for the Barbara Brennan School.

In the process, I developed a niche for myself as a healer. Although I continued to give healings to clients facing a variety of issues in their lives, I began to see a new kind of client. Women who were pregnant, or seeking to be pregnant, began to call me from around the country, and around the world. They felt the call, as I had, to try to communicate with their preborn children.

I learned that, indeed, anyone could do these exercises. What they might get out of them would vary. One woman, a massage therapist, was able to dialogue with her baby and write down pages of information about her child's purpose in life and how best to raise him. Other women received information about what they needed to eat during pregnancy, the baby's gender, and the baby's name. A couple of women even discovered that the baby was in distress and how they could help. Other women picked up only sensations, but these were strong enough, and specific enough, to make a kind of conversation.

In every case, the time that a woman spent with her baby, attempting one-on-one communication, seemed to make an enormous difference to the baby. Time and time again, women received communications that all the baby needed was her love and attention. Just the effort to communicate, and the time set aside from a busy schedule to be with the baby, seemed enormously appreciated and desired by all the children involved.

These conversations were especially helpful to women who had fears of labor and delivery, or worries about being mothers. Nearly all of them received some kind of assurance from the baby that the birth would go well, or that they themselves would be capable mothers—sometimes along with hints on how to make the birth or the parenting easier. The women profited enormously from these reassurances— and since they then relaxed and felt more confident—so did the babies.

I have been surprised to discover how natural this kind of communication has been for my clients. Women of very different backgrounds and experiences were able to access the connection with their baby and carry on deep and meaningful conversations. I frequently discovered that my prejudices about who might find these exercises difficult were dashed to the ground, as women with absolutely no formal training in using their intuitive abilities easily connected with and conversed with their preborn children.

For some women, communication with their babies before birth, though it came easily, was never comfortable. Such communication was outside their belief systems, or counter to their religious beliefs. Others were uncomfortable with their own intuitive abilities. Though I urged them to try these exercises at home by themselves, some women were only comfortable talking with their preborn children if I was present to hold the space for them.

It is my hope that this book and its exercises can hold a space for any woman, or any man, who wishes to communicate with a child soon to be born, be that child *in utero* or not yet conceived.

Why should you, as a future parent, spend time trying to communicate with your child before birth? Is it just a fun thing to do? Or do the reasons go deeper than that? Let's explore that in the next chapter.

Before you read on, take a few minutes to try the following grounding exercise. Don't make the mistake of skipping it because you think it's not important! It's probably the most important exercise in this book. Before you can be with your child, you must be here, that is, be present on earth. This is especially important if you have a natural talent for being psychic, or if you are an intellectual. Some people (myself included) have a tendency to be well connected spiritually or mentally, but less connected to the earth. If you are one of these people, practicing grounding will be crucial for you—and your baby. A baby who is trying to grow into a physical body needs a mother who is fully present in her own body. So I encourage you to practice the following exercise and make it the basis for your communication with your child. Good luck and have fun!

☙

Grounding Exercise

Find a comfortable place to sit, where you can have both feet on the ground and sit fairly upright, but comfortably enough to sit still for some time.

1.   Close your eyes and begin to relax.

2.   Feel yourself sitting in the chair. Feel the floor beneath your feet.

3.   Take three deep, slow breaths. As you breathe out, make a little sigh or some other sound.

4.   Now imagine, as you continue relaxing, that all of your energy is sliding down through your body into your feet. Imagine that your feet are actually sinking into the floor.

5.   Do you feel yourself fully in your feet? Do your feet feel heavy? Or do you feel as if you are holding yourself above the floor?

If you feel completely in your feet, continue to the next step. If not, take a moment to take each of your feet in your hands (probably by crossing each ankle over your knee in turn). Hold your foot in your hands and simply invite yourself to come completely down into your foot. Make sure you come all the way into your toes and heels— you might want to hold each of these areas in turn to accomplish this. Do this with both feet, allowing yourself to relax more and more, until you feel you are in your feet. Then continue to the next step.

6. Now imagine there is a line of light going from the bottom of each of your feet into the floor.

7. Imagine these lines of light sinking into floorboards, going through the rest of the house or building, and going into the soil.

8. Let the lines of light go deep into the soil and connect with the bedrock of the earth. Imagine them going right through the bedrock, deep into the bowels of the earth. Let them sink into the viscous rock that lies deep in the mantle of the earth. See if you can feel the warmth of that viscous rock coming up to meet you.

9. Finally, imagine these two lines of light connected to your feet actually penetrating the solid nickel core of earth. Feel that connection deep in the center of the earth. For a moment imagine yourself resting in the core of the earth, the same way a baby rests inside her mother. See if you can feel how the earth knows everything you need and supplies it in abundance. Take a moment to feel gratitude for clean water to drink, abundant air to breathe, for the plants and animals that sustain you.

This exercise is a good prelude to any kind of meditation or inner seeking exercise. It is also an excellent way to relax and connect to yourself and the earth. Please do this exercise every time before you begin the other exercises in this book. As you become adept at grounding, you will find that you can do this exercise quickly and easily.

Note: Working on the computer tends to deground us. Walking or other exercise brings us back into our bodies. Try to time your sessions with your baby at a time when you feel relaxed and grounded — although it is also a good way to get relaxed and grounded!

Chapter Two

THE CONSCIOUS CHILD

"The newborn has no past and therefore no psychology," writes Louise Kaplan in *Oneness and Separateness*, her 1978 treatise on Margaret Mahler's work.[1] When I first read these words, I had no reason to question them. Kaplan's treatise was a child psychology standard, and I found much that was helpful and important in her book.

But as I began to do research for my senior thesis in the spring of 2000, I began to uncover another view.

I went looking for evidence in the scientific realm of communication with babies *in utero*. What I found changed the way I viewed preborn and newborn babies forever. Unbeknownst to me, and I suspect to most parents and potential parents in the U.S., there is a whole field of psychology dedicated to babies just born and in the womb. More prevalent in Europe and Canada than in the U.S., the relatively new field of pre- and perinatal psychology sees newborn and preborn infants as conscious, intelligent beings, capable of communicating and of learning, with an enormous ability to sense and understand what's happening around them—sometimes a better sense than the adults in the room.

Most interesting to me, these scientists had conducted

---

[1] Kaplan, Louise, *Oneness and Separateness* (Touchstone, 1978), p. 68.

studies that seemed to prove that babies *in utero* were psychically tuned into their mothers' thoughts and feelings, and that the mother's general psychological attitude affected the baby for the rest of her life, *beginning in the womb.*

These psychologists maintained that the most formative period of life for human beings is *not* the period from birth to three years old, but the period *from conception to birth.* Whatever traumas occur at birth, some important figures in this field believe, are in fact only echoes of traumas that have already occurred in the womb.

From the beginning, the baby is linked to the mother, her moods and rhythms, her habitual thought forms and emotions. That doesn't mean that every single thought and feeling a mother experiences has a lasting impact on her child, notes Dr. Thomas Verny, a leader in the field of pre- and perinatal psychology. He says it is the consistent day-to-day pattern of thoughts and emotions that will help mold the character of your baby. "What I'm talking about is a clear-cut, continual pattern of behavior," he says. "...A physically difficult birth with its attendant emotional strains does not change things. It is what you want and feel and communicate to the baby that matters."[2]

A mother who feels good about herself, her partner, and her situation in life will communicate that to her baby. The baby will know, while still in utero, without being told. Even more importantly, the baby will know how you feel about her. And she'll know your unconscious feelings, as well as your conscious ones.

Gerhard Rottman, a professor at the University of Salzburg, Austria, actually did an experiment to prove that.[3] He studied 141 mothers-to-be. He gave the mothers psychological tests and divided them into four groups. The Ideal Mothers desired their infants both consciously and

---

[2] Verny, Thomas, *The Secret Life of the Unborn Child* (Dell Publishing 1981), p. 29.
[3] Verny, pp. 48-49.

unconsciously. The Catastrophic Mothers had clear problems with bringing children into their lives.

The Ambivalent Mothers appeared to the world, including their closest family members, to be very happy about being pregnant. But psychological testing showed that they actually had very mixed feelings about becoming mothers.

The last group, which Rottman called Cool Mothers, expressed doubts about being pregnant—they had careers, financial problems, didn't feel ready. But testing revealed that subconsciously they desired their children.

The results of the experiment are very interesting. Predictably, the Ideal Mothers produced the healthiest babies, physically and psychologically. The Catastrophic Mothers, who suffered the most serious medical problems during pregnancy, bore the group of most emotionally disturbed children.

But the most interesting results came with the other two groups of mothers. Evidently, the babies picked up on the mixed feelings of their mothers. The babies of the Ambivalent Mothers had a high number of behavioral and gastrointestinal problems. The babies of the Cool Mothers tended to be apathetic and lethargic.

In other words, the babies knew what their mothers were saying and broadcasting to the world, and what they were really feeling deep inside—and the difference. Of course, what this study did not reveal were the energetic cord problems that may have resulted from the mothers' ambivalent feelings—which no doubt played a role in the babies' physical and psychological problems.

To me this study shows that the biggest problem for the children of the last two groups was the difference between what their mothers were saying and what they were really feeling (which the mothers themselves perhaps did not even know). That's where Mother-Baby Bonding comes into play.

In the process of preparing to communicate with your baby, many of your feelings about motherhood, about yourself as a mother, and about your baby may become clear. Not all of these feelings may be ones you would like to see. That's okay. Give yourself credit for discovering the feelings. It's so important for you to be cognizant of all your feelings about the possibility of having a baby. Now you can work with them.

For example, if you feel thrilled to be pregnant, and then discover that you have some strong feelings about taking time off from your career, don't judge yourself. Allow yourself to sink into those feelings and voice them. Only by voicing them, looking at them, and seeing what's behind them will you be able to resolve them. Much, much better for your baby, as you can see from the study above, that you become conscious of your feelings and can look at them.

You might be on the other end of the spectrum. You might have many worries and concerns about having a baby. However, underneath all that, you may be feeling deep joy about the coming child. Taking time to stop and be with your baby, as you will learn to do in this book, will give you a place to receive and savor this joy.

Don't take the study above to mean that every ambivalent feeling you have about becoming a mother means your child will be a psychological wreck. Every woman has fears, doubts, and worries about becoming a mother, and some mixed feelings. We are talking here about your deep feelings that do not change from day to day.

Arthur Janov, the creator of Primal Scream Therapy, says our early emotional life—particularly in the womb and the first two years outside the womb—literally determine how our brains are hard-wired. In his 2000 book about the development of the brain and psyche, *The Biology of Love*, Janov explains how love literally makes possible the growth of the neurological system. Because the most important stage of that growth takes place in the womb, and because the child is most vulnerable at this time, Janov concludes, "The most important stage of child-rearing occurs during the nine months of pregnancy." [4]

Again and again, prenatal psychologists make the same point: What impresses us in the womb affects us more than anything will ever again in our lives. "Life is not static," Verny acknowledges. "What happens at twenty, at forty, even at sixty, certainly influences and alters us. *But it is important to point out that events affect us quite differently in the first stages of life.*" [5]

In Verny's 1981 book, *The Secret Life of the Unborn Child*, he tells the story of Boris Brott, then conductor of the Hamilton Philharmonic Symphony in Ontario, Canada. Brott related this account on a radio show:

As a young man, conducting certain pieces for the first time, he was surprised to note that he seemed to know the cello line sight unseen. Even before he turned the page, he knew how the cello line would flow. "One day I mentioned this to my mother, who is a professional cellist. I thought she'd be intrigued because it was always the cello line that was so distinct in my mind. She was; but when she heard what the pieces were, the mystery quickly solved itself. All the scores I knew sight unseen were ones she had played while she was pregnant with me." [6]

Verny also talks about working with an autistic child in a French family. Verny noted that the child responded more to spoken English than French. This was a mystery, because the family had never spoken English with their children, nor exposed them to much English. Finally, however, the mother happened to mention that, during her pregnancy, she worked in an import-export office in Paris where only

---

[4] Janov, Arthur, *The Biology of Love* (Prometheus Books, 2000), p. 198.
[5] Verny, p. 25.
[6] Verny, p. 23.

English was spoken.[7]

So don't think of the nine months of pregnancy simply as a time for preparing for being a mother when your baby is born. If you are pregnant, you are already a mother, and the most important time of your baby's life, in terms of psychological and neurological—that means mental, emotional, spiritual and physical—development is happening right now.

That puts Mother-Baby Bonding in a whole new light. It is a lovely thing to do, simply to connect your heart with your baby's. But keep in mind that your baby's growth in every way will be enhanced *for the rest of her life* by your efforts to connect with her, express your love, and help her understand the world around her while she is in the womb. The following exercise will show you how to get started.

If you are not pregnant yet, you don't have to wait until you are pregnant to communicate with your baby. If you would like to be a mother, or a father, you can start connecting with your little one today. We'll talk about that in the next chapter.

⟨❧⟩

Exercise to Connect with Your Baby During Pregnancy

This initial exercise is for women who are already pregnant. If you are planning to conceive a baby, please read the next chapter and try the exercise following that chapter.

Find a comfortable place to sit, where you can put both feet on the ground, but remain fairly upright, yet comfortable enough to stay sitting for a while. Once you get used to this exercise, you may want to try it lying in bed, or sitting cross-legged outside in the backyard, or whatever way works for you.

---

[7] Verny, p. 33.

If possible, make sure that you will not be disturbed. Turn your cell phone off, turn off the ringer on your home phone, explain to family members you will be unavailable for few minutes, or just go to a quiet place in the house.

1. Do a short grounding exercise as explained in Chapter One.

2. Once you feel grounded and relaxed, place your hands on your belly and take a few deep breaths.

3. Imagine that your hands are sinking into your belly and actually going into your womb and around your baby.

4. Just rest for a few minutes, breathing and holding your baby, and enjoy being with your baby.

5. As you do this, open up your heart (it's probably wide open already!) and send love to your baby.

6. Now, tune into your hands and see if you can sense your baby in any way. As we discussed in Chapter One, babies have an energy field, just as you do. Each baby has its own unique personality and own unique field. Can you feel this baby's particular vibration? How does it feel? Loving? Cuddly? Bouncy? Peaceful? Happy? Eager to communicate with you? Or just warm? Or cool? What do you sense?

7. Everybody has their own way of sensing energy. Some people feel sensations. Some people see colors. Some people feel emotions. Some people get pictures in their minds. Some people even get certain smells or tastes in their mouths. Some people will get a combination of above. Whatever way you are picking up your baby's energy, it is the right way. Remember, this is very subtle work. Please pay attention to any and every sensation, no matter how subtle. Say to yourself in your mind or out loud whatever sensation you are picking up

so you are sure you are aware of all that you perceiving.

8.   If you think you don't feel anything, just your own love for the baby, that's totally fine. The best gift you can give your baby is to spend some quiet time with her, just being with her and sending her love. And remember, just because you don't sense her this time, does not mean you won't another time! Don't be discouraged. You are doing great.

9.   Now, if you haven't already, frame some words in your mind to your baby. Whatever comes to you, whatever you want to say to your little one, say it right now. You can say it in your mind, or you can say it out loud. The baby will get it either way. If you are in the third trimester of your pregnancy, you might want to say it out loud, because that baby is now physically hearing you.

10.   After you have said whatever you want to say to your baby, "listen" for a response. Do you feel any energy coming back at you? Some women will actually hear words in response. Some will feel a returning emotion or sense of love. Some will see a color. Some will feel nothing at all. Any of these is great.

11.   Continue your dialogue or just being with your baby as long as you wish. When you are ready to stop, be sure to say something to let the baby know you are finishing this intimate dialogue and you will do it again soon. Take a moment for a tender farewell—which of course is not a farewell at all, since the baby is always with you. But you are ending this dialogue, and the baby needs to feel that ending clearly.

Congratulations! You have just finished your first Mother-Baby Bonding Before Birth conversation with your baby! Good for you for finding the time in your busy life to spend time with your baby. You have given your baby a very precious gift.

If you felt any sensations or heard any messages from your baby, you might want to take few moments to record those, so you have a record of your ongoing dialogue.

For ideas on how to deepen the conversation with your baby, please see Chapter Four.

Chapter Three

CONVERSATIONS BEFORE CONCEPTION

It is the first day of fall, a good time for beginning new things. I enter my meditation room and sit down. As I ground my feet into the earth, I immediately fill up with emotion and tears. One voice says, "I don't want another baby. I don't want any more sleepless nights." But I know this is just my habitual resistance to receiving, my "no" to the bigger "yes" that I feel filling the room.

I connect to this deeper, bigger feeling. A sacred presence fills the room. I feel my openness to letting the baby come in—a receptivity. It doesn't feel as though this baby is coming to me, but to the whole family—me, my husband, my son.

As I ground myself deep into the center of the earth, tears well up again, as I feel the support and softness of The Mother. Grounding has never felt so soft. I am aware of the Earth as an entity, almost as a personality, supporting me and wrapping her softness around me.

Now I focus on the connection. I hear my voice saying, as I say so often to my clients, "Imagine there is a cord coming out of your heart. It comes out of your heart,

*goes out into the room, and connects to your baby, who is
floating around somewhere in the room."*

*Almost immediately, I feel a small, sweet being
connected to me on my left side. I surrender to the
sweetness of that being, that sweet, sweet feeling that a
new baby brings. Of course, in this case, it is really the
energetic baby that I am feeling, not the physical baby
itself, but the sweetness we feel in new babies is not only
the physical baby either.*

*The form elongates and solidifies. In my mind's eye,
it now looks like a beautiful young woman in flowing
clothes, reminiscent of a Greek goddess. I ask," Who are
you?"*

*The answer comes right away. "I am your next baby."
I feel strongly that this baby is a girl, but I resist that. I
want to stay open. (During my pregnancy with my son, I
was sure I had a girl at first too.)*

*I feel deeply my love and longing for this baby. At the
same time I feel my love and connection to my son. I
know that I will be able to love both.*

*I ask the baby when she should come and hear, "You'll
know when." I find myself saying internally the name,
"Kathryn." It seems to be associated with this grown-up
soul being. I don't know what that means, but I write it
down.*

*W*ith the new view given to us by pre-and perinatal
psychologists, we can see babies in the womb in a new light.
We have a clearer idea of how much babies respond to their
parents and how much they can connect and communicate
before birth. We can see that bonding does not begin with

birth, but begins long before, in the womb. But what about before conception? Does bonding begin only when the baby becomes a physical being? Or does it go back further still?

In her book *Light Emerging* Barbara Brennan discusses how conception happens energetically. Brennan says the energetic field of the baby-to-be floats just outside the mother's field before conception takes place. The baby is waiting for the chance to connect that first genetic cord with the heart of the mother. When that happens, if all else is ready energetically and physically, conception can take place.

It is important for these genetic cords to be strong and clear. Brennan says that weak genetic cords can create congenital birth defects, inherited proclivities to different diseases, and miasmas. "For example," she writes, "problems with the genetic cord connections in the fourth (heart) chakra can result in the child being born with a hole between the two heart chambers."[1]

So the quality of connection between a mother and child before conception (and a father and child, as we will discuss in Chapter Nine) can affect the baby's health and development during and after pregnancy. Furthermore, the baby is clearly present, not in physical form, but in energetic form, with the mother before conception takes place.

How long before conception is the baby present energetically? The answer is probably different for different people, but I know of several cases personally where the baby was energetically near or in the mother's energy field for a long time, perhaps years, before conception took place.

I was a second-year student at the Barbara Brennan School when I first became sure that there were energetic beings hanging around me, waiting to incarnate. I was sitting in one of our meditation and channeling sessions. The energy is very fine and delicate during these sessions, and it is

---

[1] Brennan, Barbara, *Light Emerging* (Bantam, 1993), p. 185.

easy to go to a place of heightened awareness. As I sat there cross-legged on a pillow, I became aware that there were three energetic children sitting around me. One was in my lap, another was leaning against me on one side, and a third one was sitting under my arm on the other side. I felt exactly as you might feel sitting at a lecture with your three children sitting around you. Later I had dreams that I had three children—two boys and one girl. (So far, we have one boy, we have lost one in miscarriage, and are thinking about having another.)

Several mothers in my senior thesis study had similar stories to tell. Lisa, a 41-year-old attorney in family law, wanted to become pregnant for about two years before she actually conceived. During these two years she felt the baby's energy field almost like a physical presence. She said she felt as though some unseen person was standing close to her. The presence felt like a baby to her, soft and tender. This feeling of tenderness helped open all the tenderness inside of her. She wanted to reach out and hold the child.

On an energetic level, we might say that feeling the energetic presence of her baby helped Lisa to open that place deep in her heart where the genetic cord could connect, allowing conception to take place.

Lisa did this naturally, easily, without help. But in my practice, I work regularly with women who have had trouble allowing this connection to occur. Some of these women have been trying to get pregnant for years. Some of them already have children. But, for one reason or another, they are having trouble making a connection with the child wanting to incarnate.

Sometimes the reason is quite simple, and easy to resolve. I worked with one woman who could sense the baby's energetic field near her, but could not feel any heart connection, nor make any contact with the baby. As we continued working together, the woman realized something important. The way she created reality was to visualize it. For her to enter into a new project, she first had to see it in her head. In her case, she wanted to have a home birth. She was planning to move soon, but didn't know where yet. So she didn't know where the birth was going to occur. This was creating a deep sense of insecurity in her that made it impossible for her to conceive. If she couldn't see it, she couldn't do it.

We all have our own way of creating reality. When I have a new project I am trying to manifest, I tend to talk about it to everyone I know. Usually, the more I say it, the more real it becomes. This woman had to see where she was going to be and what the birth was going to look like, otherwise she couldn't create her pregnancy. She realized she needed to either move, or at least decide where she was going to move, before she could conceive a baby. That was a great relief to her, not only to give herself permission to have those conditions before she conceived, but also to realize that her block to pregnancy was quite concrete, and easy to resolve. She could do something about it.

The interesting part of the story is what happened next. As soon as she got clear about this issue, she was able to connect to the baby, and had an in-depth conversation with her child-to-be.

I always tell my clients: You are the only one who knows what you need in order to be a mother. The client above may have had some sense before the session that not knowing where she was going to birth was a problem for her. She either didn't pay attention to how important that was, or decided it was "silly." If you know you need certain conditions to feel comfortable getting pregnant, listen to that voice. Nobody knows what you need to feel okay about being a mother. Nothing is too "silly."

I worked with another woman who already had one child, but wanted another. She had already had several different kinds of medical intervention, but nothing had worked.

At the beginning of her session, she could not sense the energetic presence of the baby at all, nor feel any kind of heart connection with the child. I tried every way I knew to try to connect her with her baby, or help her sense the baby's field, but nothing worked. Finally I did something I try to avoid doing at the beginning of a session. I shared with her my own perceptions. "Well, there is a baby in your field," I said to her. As soon as she heard these words, the mother started sobbing. She had become so used to trying not to hope, in order not to feel disappointed, that she could no longer feel her own longing for a child. In other words, she was so worried about not being able to conceive that she had blocked off her connection to her child—the very thing that would help her to conceive!

As soon as she received confirmation that a baby was indeed floating around her energetically, trying to connect, the flood gates opened. She opened that space deep in her heart, and felt her connection to her baby, and all the softness and tenderness of her own heart. Those are exactly the kind of conditions needed for conception.

Another woman could sense the baby's field, but rather far from her. She felt the baby was actually outside the house, just outside the window. As she conversed with the child, the baby came closer into her field. She conceived a few months later.

The conversation between a mother and a child waiting to become physical varies, just as it does between a woman who is already pregnant and her baby in the womb. Some women simply feel the qualities of softness, tenderness, playfulness, or calmness, depending on the character of the baby. Other women sense answers to yes or no questions. Some women can carry on long, detailed conversations with their baby-to-be.

Sheila was a 41-year-old marriage and family therapist.

She had been trying to conceive for about a year. As we began the session, she found the energetic baby in her field immediately. She perceived it as sleeping, however, and not willing to wake up for conversation.

Since she was seeing the energetic baby, but not fully connecting with it, I suggested she look around for another presence. You may have different names for this presence, depending on your beliefs and experiences. Once the baby is physical, energy healers call this presence a spiritual guide. My work with babies has led me to believe that this spiritual guide is also who we are before we become physical beings. Some people may call this being the soul of the baby.

At any rate, I asked Sheila to sense into the room and see if she could feel such a presence. She quickly identified a tall being without a precise gender, but clearly present. As she conversed with this being about why she had not yet conceived a baby, she began to understand that, for her, conception was a process that would take some time. This session was part of that process. Mostly what she needed to do was "just relax" and stop being impatient with herself.

As she absorbed this information, something happened inside of Sheila. She softened and relaxed and let down her guard. She began to cry. As she cried, the energetic baby woke up and aligned himself directly in front of her heart. He asked to come close to her and be in her arms. "I've been waiting a long time for you," he told her.

Sheila talked for a long time with her baby and her baby's guide. She received a lot of information, including her baby's name, his purpose in life, and some tips for raising him. But the most important moment of the session was the moment when she relaxed into her process, accepted herself where she was, and let go of her anxiety. The minute she did that, her heart opened, and the baby was able to connect with her energetically.

The following exercise will show you how to connect with

your baby, if you are even thinking about conceiving a child. It doesn't matter if you have been trying to conceive for a long time or have only just considered it. Clients often ask me, "Do you ever do a session and there is no one there to talk to?" My answer is always, "Never." If you are even thinking about having a baby, there is a baby waiting to talk to you.

Before you begin this exercise, make sure you are grounded by doing the exercise following Chapter One or whatever exercise you have devised yourself for becoming grounded. Make sure you turn off your phone, television, radio, and computer, and that you will not be disturbed during your session. I would also advise you not to be in the same room, or at least not very close to, any computers or televisions that have been operating recently. These machines have quite strong electrical and magnetic fields of their own that affect the space around them for several hours after they have been turned off.

If you are trying to conceive a child, and have experienced a miscarriage, stillbirth or abortion in the past, you may want to read Chapter 10 and do the exercises following that chapter to bring closure to your relationship with that child. Of course, you may find the same energetic child is hanging around you, waiting to be conceived! Or a completely different child may be waiting to incarnate. Either way, you may find it easier to conceive once you have brought closure to your previous pregnancy.

⤐

Exercise for Connecting with Your Baby Before Conception

1. Take a few minutes to do the grounding exercise at the end of Chapter One. Make sure you feel very rooted and connected to the earth.

2. Now take a moment to center yourself in your heart.

Breathe. Let your heart open, like a flower opening to the sun. Picture your baby, the little one you would like to bring into your life, and let your heart open to him.

3. Imagine a cord coming out of your heart, going out into the room and connecting with your little one, wherever he is in the room. Gently breathe while you let that cord connection get stronger and more solid.

4. Imagine you are sending your love down through this cord to your baby. Try to feel at what point in the cord you feel the energy of your baby coming back to you in return.

5. If you don't feel your baby through this cord connection method, simply ask yourself where in the room you feel your baby. Don't think too much or question what you sense, or worry about being right or wrong, or whether you are making it up, simply go with what you feel.

6. Whichever method you used, take some time now to sense into your baby. Simply breathe and connect with your baby's energy. Feel into your baby's energy. What is it like? How would you describe it? Light or dense? Soft or active? Buzzing? Quiet? Every baby is unique. How does this baby feel to you?

7. Take a few moments to just breathe and be with your baby. See if you can attune yourself to your baby's energy and create even more connection between you.

8. When you are ready, send a message of greeting to your baby. What would you like to say to your energetic child? Let him know whatever is in your heart to say.

Sometimes these moments of connection can be quite emotional. Whatever you feel, please let yourself just feel it. If you feel like crying, please let yourself cry. Whatever you feel—tenderness, longing, frustration about waiting for a child—whatever it is, let it flow through you.

9. After sending a message to your energetic baby, take some time to see if you receive any kind of reply. This could be anything—a feeling of love, a picture in your mind, a sensation. You may even hear words—but you may not. Your reply may be something much more subtle—a vibration, a shift in the energy that you sense.

10. Let this first communication with your baby just be about developing the connection between you and your child, and learning to sense the baby's energy. In the next chapter, we will talk about asking the baby specific questions.

11. When you are ready to stop, let your baby know you are going to end the dialogue now, but you will take time for another chat in the near future. Take a moment for a tender farewell—which of course is not a farewell at all, since the baby is always with you. But you are ending this dialogue, and the baby needs to feel that ending clearly.

After your session you might want to jot down a few notes in a journal or notebook, so you have a continuing record of your conversation with your child.

Chapter Four

DEVELOPING
A CONVERSATION
WITH YOUR BABY

*C*ongratulations! You have taken that first important step of connecting with your baby. Now you are ready to begin an ongoing conversation that will last the rest of your life. Whether you are already pregnant or planning to conceive, try to make these exercises a regular practice. How often will be up to you. I usually recommend at least once a week, but for some busy women, twice a month may be good. Of course, if you can connect with your baby every day, that's ideal—for you and the baby. But don't sweat it if you can't do these exercises as often as you'd like. Don't make connecting with your baby one more "should" on a list of things to do. Let it be a joyful experience that you do when you can.

Lisa, the 41-year-old family law attorney, used these exercises—and her own profound sensitivity—to develop a deep and delightful relationship with her daughter long before birth. Three months into her pregnancy, mother and daughter were communicating regularly, expressing their love for each other, receiving mutual assurance, and enjoying each other's presence. After her second Mother-Baby Bonding session, Lisa wrote in her journal, "I 'saw' her

next to me on my right side, then flashed a vision. We were
lying together on a beach. She was curled up next to me. We
were absorbing the earth energy and just enjoying it. I could
see some interesting matrix forms that embodied the energy.
She opened her eyes and looked at me. I sent some loving
energy."

Lisa spent the next few sessions of exercises "energetically
stroking" her baby, which the baby seemed to enjoy. As
time went on, the baby also seemed to get more used to the
stroking and better able to respond. Lisa notes during the
second week of sessions, "She was very alert this time, in a
more physical manner. More than the previous times. She
quieted down the more I stroked her. There is a more direct
and knowing response now to what I am doing."

Catherine, a 35-year-old technical writer, found that her
conversations with her baby not only gave them a better
connection before he was born, but also prepared her for
spending time with him after his birth. At the moment of his
birth, she said, "I felt like I already knew him…We already
had a relationship established." She felt more connected to
her son "in a bodily way," she said. "Why, here he is. This is
you, you've been inside me."

As you can see, the most precious aspect of connecting with
your baby—and the most important—is the exchange of love
and energy between the two of you. But sometimes these
conversations can yield important or interesting information.

Conception

If you are waiting to conceive a child, you may have
questions about how soon you will conceive, or when the
best time to conceive is. If you have been trying for a long
time to have a child, you may want to ask for the baby's
input.

I am in no way advising you to ignore or leave out crucial
consultations with your medical doctors. However, in my

experience, the baby often has a helpful perspective.

In your next conversation, you may also want to explore some of the topics below, whether or not you have conceived yet. The more you talk to your baby, the more information you have, the more real your baby is to you. In other words, the more developed your relationship with your energetic baby is, the better your chances of conceiving.

The Baby's Health

The most important question for any mother bearing a child is whether the baby is healthy. These days most women avail themselves of ultrasound and other tests to answer this question.

I have mixed feelings about the use of ultrasound during pregnancy. On the one hand, it is responsible for yielding much of the information we have about preborn babies and what they are really like. It can permit early detection and helpful intervention for children with birth defects. On the other hand, research shows that ultrasound is not the best thing for your baby. Researchers have found that that ultrasound may cause chromosome damage, DNA breakdown, and other changes in circulation, liver cells, brain enzymes, nerve reflexes, and emotional reactivity.[1] After a study at the University of South Florida on children exposed to ultrasound *in utero*, researchers advised pregnant women to reject ultrasound as a diagnostic procedure. The leading researcher said "he would personally not consider using ultrasound at any time during pregnancy." [2]

Having said that, the decision to use ultrasound, just like the decision to have a baby, is a very personal one. My decision, based mostly on my own instincts (which told me such a procedure would not be good for my baby), was to forgo any ultrasound. This left me in the unenviable position

---

[1] Verny, Thomas, The Psycho-Technology of Pregnancy and Labor, *Pre- and Perinatal Psychology Journal*, 1(1), Spring 1986, p. 38.
[2] Ibid, p. 39.

of not knowing exactly how my baby was doing. Except that I did know. Every time I did a session, I asked the baby how he was. The answer always came back that he was fine. I also had a deep knowing—despite several fantastical fears—that everything *was* fine.

Let's say a word about those fantastical fears. Every mother has them. Well, maybe there are some calm and levelheaded women who don't, but I did. My first fear, for some inexplicable reason, was that my child's fingers and toes would not be fully formed. This was based partially on misinformation. In my mind these digits would be the last part of my baby's body to form. It wasn't until several months into my pregnancy that I discovered the truth: The baby's toes and fingers begin forming in week five and, by week 10, are already forming finger nails. The part of the body that actually forms last, and that you need to worry about if you have a premature baby, is the lungs. (That makes sense, if you think about it. The baby's been living in water, breathing your oxygen. It's not until birth that she needs to breathe on her own.) Somehow, once I knew that the digits actually form fairly early on in the process, I didn't worry about them so much.

Don't ask me why, but the next fear I had about my baby's health involved his head—or heads, as it were. I was afraid he would be born with two heads. I don't know where I got this idea. Reading Greek myths as a child? Maybe it actually reflected my own process—the way I stay too much in my head.

What I should have done is put these fears to rest by asking my baby about them. I didn't think of doing that, but you can. Whatever your fears are about your baby's health, however grounded or not, ask. Ask your baby if there is anything you need to know about her health. Ask specific questions about each fear you hold.

The Gender Question

Are you carrying a boy or a girl? It's rather funny to watch your friends and family trying to make predictions. And even those parents who avail themselves of the ultrasound may find—every now and then—that the information they received was not, shall we say, the whole picture.

During her pregnancy, Gerry, a 31-year-old mother of a 21-month-old son, said she knew her baby was a boy by his vibration. "I had named him and spoke to him throughout my pregnancy. He seemed to 'perk' up in my belly whenever I spoke with him. I envisioned a picture of him in my head straining to hear what I was saying and yet so blissfully content within the womb at the same time. He was a definite distinct presence in my body, not alien or obtrusive, just was, and it felt divine. I felt very honored to be carrying such a precious entity within me."

Danielle is a hospital administrator and energy healer. She was two-and-a-half months pregnant with her daughter when she spontaneously began receiving communications from the baby. She recalled, "I was at home sitting on the couch dealing with some insurance papers with the TV set on in the background for company. In the next second—or actually it did not even register in 'time'—I 'heard' my baby tell me that her name was Katie and that she was a large girl, so that I could be prepared." Danielle had never heard of anyone communicating with her baby before birth. The experience shocked and frightened her. She immediately shut down her ability to receive further communications from the baby. However, six months later, she gave birth to a nine-and-a-half-pound baby girl by Cesarean section and named her Katie.

It's quite common for my clients to receive information as to whether they are carrying a boy or a girl during their sessions. Usually they get some kind of vision of the baby Sometimes the baby tells them. If you want to know, just ask!

Finding the Baby's Name

As you can see from Danielle's experience, another important piece of information that can come from these sessions is the baby's name. A client once told me that her mother asked her, while she was pregnant, if she had found the baby's name. "Every baby comes with its own name," the mother reportedly said. "You just have to find it." I had never heard this piece of wisdom, but it certainly fits with my own personal experience and the experiences of my clients.

I received my son's name, Jacob, in a guidance session at the Monroe Institute, a center in Central Virginia founded by Robert Monroe, which trains people to use different brain wavelength configurations. I was seven months pregnant at the time, and I had asked for guidance about what I could do to make the impending birth easier. I heard, "Call the baby by his name," and had a vision of myself in the last stages of labor, calling, "Jacob, Jacob, Jacob!" I came out of the session thinking, "What is this old-fashioned name?" I didn't like it at all. The only people I knew named Jacob were in their sixties or seventies. (Little did I know that Jacob would be the most popular name for newborn boys in the United States for at least 11 years before and after my son's birth!)

I shelved the name for the time being, but it was too late. It began to grow on me. By the time my son was born, he was Jacob in my heart.

If you have already picked out a name that you love, honor that. But be sensitive to your baby. I've heard many people say it's best to pick the baby's name once you see the baby. But if you do your Mother-Baby Bonding Sessions regularly, you will already have a good sense of this baby and her personality. And you can simply ask your baby in a session what her name is! You may or may not hear something precise. In that case, you can try something easier. Ask yes or no questions. Ask the baby how she likes different names and see what response you feel coming back.

Raising Your Baby

No one is an expert on your child the way your baby is before birth. She's the best one to ask what makes her unique and what her special needs are. If you want to know how best to raise your child, ask her. I learned this from one of my clients named Joy. An expectant mother in Ohio, she received a plethora of information about her baby and how to raise her in her Mother-Baby Bonding Session. This was partly because she was naturally gifted at this kind of communication, but also simply because she asked.

"Be open and listen to me," her baby told her. "Let me come to you with my problems, whatever they may be. Don't judge what's happening, just be there to listen."

The baby also had some advice for her father. "Make me laugh," she said. "Show me more physical things—the earth, sports—that will ground me."

The baby reminded my client that, as a mother, she still needed to live her own life. "Take time for yourself," she urged. "Leave me with Dad or someone else. Get away."

Another child told his mother, a therapist in California, not to get into power struggles. "It's important to hold the line." He also spoke about the importance of the relationship between the parents. "It's really important to value the relationship with my father," he said. "Give that the time it needs. Don't sacrifice that for the child. It's all one relationship to the child. Always make sure there's time for enjoyment together."

Catherine, the technical writer mentioned earlier, was a third-year student at the Barbara Brennan School while she was pregnant. During the summer she had to decide whether she could work full-time, finish her last year of school, and still be the mother she wanted to be. So she asked the baby in her next session. "What do you really need?" The answer kept coming back: "Time, and for the focus to be on me and not on other stuff."

"He was telling me to slow down and not to be doing too many things at the same time, because he was going to be needing me," Catherine said later. She knew she would have to go back to work three or four months after her baby's birth. She decided, after this conversation with her unborn son, not to go back to school. "I've wanted to have a child for a few years. The first years are so important. Why would I divide myself?"

Sometimes a client in a first session cannot hear words, but receives impressions and feelings. In those cases, I can sometimes hear the specific words that the baby is saying. One client in Scotland saw colors when she asked questions. When she asked for advice on raising her baby, I heard these words, "You are the perfect parents for me. Your light and your energy drew me. I am a baby prepared to step into a certain inheritance—an inheritance of grace and love and light."

The baby continued, "As you raise me, please remember my path is with you, but not of you. I have my own path. There will be times that you want to make things easier for me, or pave the way for me—but those are not your times to help. Those are my times and I have to do it alone--with your support, of course, but by myself. I will need less help that you might believe. Those are my challenges to learn by."

Sometimes the client and I both receive words from the baby. The 50-year-old therapist who wanted to know if it was possible to have a first baby heard, "This soul will raise itself. I won't need to know anything. I just need to hold the space, and the baby will raise itself. I just need to provide a loving atmosphere, but don't need to know how to do anything."

I told her I felt the baby needed lots of space. She shouldn't have any expectations about this child, because he would rebel against such expectations. Growing up, he would do lots of experimentation, lots of hands-on activity—a child that would get into everything, "I will get dirty a lot—let me!" he said. "Messy, messy, messy!"

What does your child need? Every being is different. In your next session, try asking your baby what you need to know about raising her.

⊂⊗⊃

Exercise to Develop Your Conversation with Your Baby

In this exercise you will begin to carry on a more detailed conversation with your baby. You will begin practicing asking specific questions and listening for the answers.

This process will be very different for different women. Some women will be able to hear words from their babies right away. Some women will feel sensations or vibrations, see a picture or color in their mind, or even smell an odor. Some women may feel no response of any kind.

If you hear your baby replying in words, or see a picture in your mind of her answering right away, that's great. Try to keep a journal of what you hear and see.

If you feel sensations or vibrations, that's fabulous. Though less specific, these feelings in the body are often more accurate than words or pictures. Let me say a word about receiving sensations or vibrations. Sometimes women tell me they are picking nothing up from their baby, but if I probe a little more, I discover they are actually feeling all kinds of things, but they do not recognize these feelings. Remember this is subtle work. Do not discount anything you feel. A feeling of warmth, a feeling of love or tenderness, even a buzzing is a sensation you are receiving in your body, a kinesthetic perception of your baby. Pay attention to those subtle sensations, stick with them, explore them, let them grow stronger and more specific. Don't ignore anything you are picking up.

If you are receiving answers in sensations or vibrations, how do you get answers to specific questions? One way is to ask "yes" or "no" questions. Most of us can identify fairly easily the difference between a "yes" current and a "no" current. You might start by asking yourself a very simple question that you already know the answer to so you can feel the difference between a "yes" and a "no" current in your body. For example, you might ask yourself, "Is my name Judy?" or "Do I live in Iowa?" Try asking yourself a "yes" question and a "no" question a few times so you know how these two different currents feel in your body.

If you are perceiving, as some women do, odors or tastes or colors in your mind, that's great. Make notes of the specific smells/colors/tastes you perceive in answer to which questions. Over time, you may begin to establish patterns and understand what these perceptions mean in answer to your questions.

Again, don't think too much. Don't worry about whether you are making it all up. I've never done a session with a mother-to-be which felt to me as though she were making it up. (Remember, I am an energy healer, so I practice perceiving energy every day in my professional work.) Even if you were making it all up in the beginning, so what? You are still spending time with and focusing on your baby, and she knows it. With practice, you will find yourself carrying on a conversation, whether in words or not.

Once again, make sure you are in a comfortable sitting position, but with your feet on the ground, and in a place where you won't be disturbed by people or electronic communications.

One word about the grounding exercise. If you feel that you are not fully grounded, even though you do the grounding exercise, you may want to do some physical exercise before you try these exercises with your baby. There is nothing like physical exercise—particularly weight-bearing exercise like walking, running or dancing—to get you in your feet and connected to the earth.

1.   Do the grounding exercise and make sure you feel connected to the earth.

2.   If you are connecting with an energetic baby (preconception), connect to your baby using the cord from your heart, or just by sensing in the room where your baby is. If you are connecting with a physical baby in the womb, place your hands on your belly and imagine they are sinking into the womb until they are gently holding your baby.

3.   Take a moment to breathe and feel your baby's energy. Just enjoy being with your baby for a few moments. (If you never feel any response to your questions, just these first three steps are the most important, and will make so much difference to your baby.)

4.   Greet your baby and send some words her way. Pay attention to what kind of a response you feel. Is it a picture? Words? A sensation or feeling? A smell? Honor whatever way you perceive.

5.   If you are actually hearing words from your baby, I would suggest at this point you ask your baby if she has anything to say to you. Often when we ask only specific questions, we miss out on important or interesting things the baby might say to us if we just ask. Even if you are not hearing words, I would ask whether the baby has anything to communicate with you and see what you get.

6.   The question above may lead you into a dialogue with your baby. But if you want to ask specific questions,

please do.

If you are preparing for conception, you can ask when the best time is for you to conceive, what you can do to aid conception and why the baby has chosen to come to you. If you are asking "yes" and "no" questions, make your questions more specific still. *Is the coming year a good time for me to conceive? Is summer the best time? Is July the best month?* Ask a broader question, and then get more specific.

If you are already pregnant, you can ask about the baby's heath. *Is your body developing perfectly? Is there anything I need to know?* Whether you are pregnant or preparing to conceive, you can ask:

Will you be a boy or a girl?

What is your name? If you already have a name in mind, ask the baby if she likes that name and feel for the "yes" or "no" currrent. If she doesn't seem to like that one, try other names that occur to you.

Is there anything I should know about raising you? For "yes" or "no" questions, ask more specific questions. *Are you the kind of child who will need a lot of freedom? Or who likes close companions? Or both? Will you like to be with groups of people? Do you prefer one-on-one? Or will you like spending time alone?*

Are you the hunter/gatherer type, who likes to be in the woods, making things with sticks and stones? Are you more social, playing imaginary games in the house? Will you like to get dirty? Or will you like pretty clothes?

Will you be a physically active child? a daredevil? or more cautious? Are you calm? (Don't get caught in gender or other stereotypes here. My son, for example, is very physically active, but generally calm and cautious about his safety.)*Will you be musical? Will you be into sports? Will you be very artistic?*

These of course are just suggestions. This is a very personal conversation, and what you talk and ask about is up to you.

7.   As you bring your dialogue with your baby to a close, make sure you spend a moment to tenderly end the conversation and send your love one last time to your little one.

How was this conversation different from your first contact with your baby? Did you feel the baby more or less vividly? Take a few moments to record what you perceived and how you felt being with your baby.

Were you able to pick up specific answers to your questions? If so, congratulations! You are well launched into conversing with your baby.

Did you pick up "yes" and "no" currents in answer to your specific questions? That's fantastic! That's an equally valid way to dialogue with your baby.

If you don't feel like you are getting any specific answers to your questions, even "yes" or "no" answers, don't worry. You are not alone. If you are feeling your baby at all, that is the important thing. Also, practice makes perfect. Many women make the mistake of trying one time to communicate with their baby, not perceiving anything, and then saying, "Well, obviously I can't do this," and never trying again. You didn't expect yourself to come out with a perfect, long sentence the first time you tried to talk, or a perfect essay the first time you tried to write. Like everything else, learning to perceive subtle energy takes time and practice.

If connecting with your baby in sweetness and love, which is really the main point of these exercises, is enough for you and that's what you experience, that's wonderful. Please try to connect with your baby this way whenever you have time.

If you really want to communicate in words or pictures, and you haven't been able to so far, read the next chapter and try the exercises at the end of that chapter.

Chapter Five

DEEPENING THE CONVERSATION: LIFE PURPOSE AND YOUR BABY'S GUIDES

*W*hy are we here? What brings us to this blue planet hanging softly in space, this one place in the universe? Don't we all ask ourselves this question at some point in our lives? Have you answered it?

For most of us, it takes years of our life to answer this question. And we are lucky if we get the answer. But your baby, your child of light, the one who is coming to you now, he knows the answer. He knows why he is coming and why he has picked you to be his parents.

At the Barbara Brennan School we learned that a being chooses his parents before conception, depending on the kind of work his soul needs to do in that lifetime. The parents will provide the right emotional and physical environment for the being's personal task.[1]

What I have learned helping women to dialogue with their children before birth has confirmed this. The children of my clients seem to come with a personal task to accomplish, and

---

[1] Brennan, Barbara, *Hands of Light* (Bantam, 1987), p. 62.

it is often linked to the kinds of parents they have.

Joy was my first client who asked her child about his
purpose in life. She was able to hear much detailed
information about her child and her child's life. "As you
know," her baby told her, "I will be a light worker and I am
here to teach my parents" to go back toward creativity.

Together, the baby said, "We will learn how to accomplish
through our creativity. To change aspects of our minds,
expanding our mind sets. I'll teach you and you'll teach me
about universal laws that you'll need to know and I'll need
to know to accomplish some of this."

According to the baby girl, she and her mother had been
mother and child before in a previous life or lives. In those
past life times, abandonment was the issue—being separated
and not being able to accomplish their life purpose together.
"We have a second chance," her daughter told Joy.

Although this baby was a first child, she told her mother
that she would someday have a brother. She went on to say
that she and her brother had had a disagreement about who
would come first. She said the power struggle between them
would continue after her birth, but there would be "great
love" between them. At the time this book was written, the
little girl was nearly three years old, but had no brother yet.
Her mother said they were talking about having another
child, but she was in massage school, and wanted to finish
that first.

As you can see, the words from Joy's daughter suggest a
dialogue occurred on another level before birth—between
the parents and child, between siblings—about the life that
was to come and its purpose. Her words even suggest that
all is not necessarily harmony at that level either, seeing
that she and her brother "had a disagreement." Long before
birth, they had already begun working on their relationship.

Another way to ask about the baby's purpose in life is to

connect with the baby's guide or guides. A Barbara Brennan student who was part of my thesis study taught me this. Although I had learned at the school to communicate with my own guides, it had never occurred to me to try to connect with the baby's guides.

There are many ways to describe these spiritual guides. Some call these nonphysical beings angels or souls. In my experience each of us is an eternal nonphysical being who makes a decision to incarnate as a physical being. Once we have incarnated as a physical being, that eternal part of us is still present, and can be communicated with.

Lisa connected to her guides and then to the baby's guides and asked them to protect the baby—literally to "take the baby out" during times when she was feeling especially emotional or was expressing her emotions. From then on, whenever she was especially emotional, she would tune in to make sure this happened. Usually she found out that the guides had already done it. She said she felt much more comfortable about being emotional while pregnant, especially feeling anger, as a result.

She also discussed her emotions with her daughter. "I explained to Cara that I loved her deeply, and although we are one, we were also separate," she wrote in her journal notes. "I explained to Cara that I needed all of my emotions, and emotions will ebb and flow like waves on the ocean. I explained that they were not directed at her, and that her guides would take her to play elsewhere, and that wasn't abandonment."

The baby replied that "she understood, and that my release of energy meant that she had more room." On another day, Lisa wrote, "She said she loved when I stroked her and keep letting my emotions flow, because it created more room for her."

The information that the mother releasing emotion was actually good for the baby because it gave the baby "more room" is interesting. It was reassuring to me, since I lost my temper more than once while pregnant.[2]

After talking with Lisa I went home and tried to connect to my own baby's guide. I found a very large nonphysical being filled with love—for me! I had never imagined someone could love me so much. For the first time I began to understand the depth of the connection between me and my son, and how much love a baby brings into the world.

That experience of profound love was immensely helpful in the days following my son's birth, when I was often exhausted and out of patience. Just the memory of that experience—and the occasional reconnection with that larger being who was my son, and yet somehow much more than him—helped me to be more loving and more patient with frequent night feedings, leaky diapers, and all the other trials of new motherhood.

In Chapter Three we talked about Sheila, who was having trouble getting a response from her baby during a Mother-Baby Bonding session with me. She could see the energetic baby but he seemed to be sleeping and not inclined to dialogue with her. So we connected with her baby's guide instead. She saw a "sort of angel" with no determinate gender standing in the room near her baby.

Sheila was not pregnant at this time. She had been trying to conceive for several years. Her baby's guide told her, "Just relax." She could feel the guide indicating that anxiety was blocking her conception. The guide said, "You're impatient,

---

[2] I don't believe it's necessary to ask the baby's guides to "take the baby out" when you are being emotional, although you may try it if you feel more comfortable feeling and expressing your emotions that way. In my experience, as long as you are conscious of your emotions and expressing them in a healthy, nonblaming way, the baby will not be harmed by emotions, even anger. The important thing is to take responsibility for your own emotions. If you bury your emotions and do not express them, then the baby will feel them and have to process them through his own developing cells. Hence Cara told Lisa that she "had more space" when her mother released her emotions.

aren't you?" Sheila made an effort to relax and laughed.
"Now I'm easier to work with," she reported the guide
saying. "Babies don't happen by will," the guide said.

As the dialogue continued, Sheila continued to relax.
Suddenly her energetic baby "woke up" and wanted to come
near her. "He wants to come and give me a hug," she said.
The baby came near and sat in her lap. As her heart opened
to him, Sheila began to cry. "I've been waiting a long time
for you," she told her baby. She saw a baby boy, wearing
little overalls with a train engine on the bib. "He just wants
to sit with me and let me hold him," she said.

As the session continued, the baby's guide helped Sheila see
that she was holding a series of beliefs that were preventing
her from conceiving a baby. The beliefs stemmed from
Sheila's childhood experiences with her own parents and
included statements such as, "The only safe people are
grandparents." A marriage and family therapist, Sheila
had already worked on her own issues many times, but
nevertheless she found herself learning new things about her
own psyche from her child's guide. The guide told her that,
despite these beliefs, she would be a good parent, "because
you are a self-correcting person."

"That's one thing he's looking forward to," the guide
informed her. "As you know, the problem is not when
parents make mistakes, but when they don't correct them."

The guide gave Sheila some advice about the best place
to raise her son. He told Sheila her baby's purpose in life
related to "making a better world" by working with the
environment. Sheila had been wondering whether she
should stay in California or move back to the east coast. The
guide advised her to stay in California, as this would be a
better place for the development of her baby's life purpose.

Like Sheila, you may find that you receive clearer answers
to some of your questions if you try talking to your baby's

guide or guides. This can be a helpful practice to develop, because even after your baby is born, it is not always easy to communicate. Once you have a newborn baby in your arms who is unable to talk to you, you may find it very helpful to connect with your baby's guide for help in raising him.

If you don't feel comfortable with the idea of connecting with guides, you can ask your baby herself, as Joy did, about his purpose in life. The following exercises will teach you how to open your chakras—your energy centers—in order to connect more deeply with your baby or with his guides.

⟋⟍⟋⟍

Journaling Your Baby's Responses

When you are asking about such deep questions as life purpose, it is possible to ask "yes" or "no" questions, but it is much more difficult, because the possibilities are endless. If you have never heard words from your baby in answer to your questions, you might want to try journaling the answer.

Keep a notebook or journal and a pen next to you as you begin the exercise below. As you start dialoguing with your baby, put the notebook or journal in your lap and write the answer. Don't think. Don't try to hear the answer first. Just write.

When you first try this, you may find yourself writing gibberish. That's okay. If you keep practicing, you may find yourself writing sentences that make sense. How do I know I am not making this up? you may ask yourself. At first you won't know. Don't worry, keep going. Even if you think you are making it all up, keep practicing. One day you will surprise yourself. You will find yourself writing something that you never could or would have thought.

You will be able to verify this information later. If you use this method to ask your child about his personality, his likes and dislikes, the best way to raise him, this is all information you can easily prove or disprove later. Every baby arrives with a distinct personality. As your baby grows, it will be easy to see if you received correct information. Then you will know that the information you received about the bigger picture—his life purpose, for example—is probably also correct.

By the way, I do not recommend telling your child what you learned about his life purpose after he is born. This is the kind of thing we all need to discover for ourselves.

It is very important to be well grounded when you are doing an exercise like the one above. It also helps to have your chakras open. The following exercise will help you open your chakras.

⬥

Exercise to Open Your Chakras

Chakras are vortices in our body and our energy field that metabolize energy. They replenish the physical body with energy. You use them when you pick up information on an energetic level. If you are hearing, smelling or tasting responses to your questions to your baby, you are using your fifth chakra, your throat chakra. If you are seeing pictures or colors, you are using your sixth chakra, that spot on your forehead between your eyes often called the third eye. If you are obtaining information by just knowing it, you may be using your seventh chakra, the chakra on the top of your head.

1. If you are pregnant, you should do the following exercise very gently. If you are advanced in your pregnancy, you may want to skip it. Do what feels right for you.

    Stand with your knees slightly bent. Rock your pelvis gently back and forth. Now move your pelvis in a circular motion, starting to the right. This opens your first chakra, which connects you to the earth. Dancing will also open your first chakra, as will any kind of physical exercise. It's important to have your first chakra open and connected to the earth. This is how you ground and receive earth energy.

As you do this exercise, imagine that your first chakra is open and reaching to the ground. A chakra is shaped like a funnel. The first chakra comes out of your pelvic floor and goes down the earth, with the wide part of the funnel between and around your feet. Let your first chakra be wide and full, and imagine that it reaches the floor or even goes into the ground a little.

As you continue circling your pelvis, imagine the earth is coming up to meet you. See if you can feel the warmth of the earth. My teachers at the Barbara Brennan School used to say, "Imagine you are sitting on a volcano. Feel the heat of the volcano." As you do this exercise, you may feel yourself getting hot.

2.   Now let's open your fifth chakra. Let your head drop forward, then backward (just a little backward—going really backward with your head can hurt your neck), to one side and then the other. Now gently roll your neck in one direction a few times, then in the other. You can also sing a song. Either of these methods will open your fifth chakra.

Now just stand or sit with your mouth slightly open. Relax your jaw. Just sit and be receptive. Being receptive means not doing anything, just opening to receive. Imagine love and light are pouring from the universe into your mouth, down your throat and into your body. Pay attention. Does the love and light get stuck at your throat? If so, try yawning a few times, or putting your hand to your throat and sending some comforting energy to your throat. Really let your throat open up and receive.

3.   To open your sixth chakra, we use the eyes. Put your

two hands together and let them carve a sideways figure 8, the symbol of infinity (∞) in space. Let it be quite big, wider than your body. Follow your hands with your eyes. Do this for a couple of minutes. This will open your sixth chakra.

4.   Finally, place your hand on top of your head and rub your crown. Imagine there is a funnel coming out of your head reaching up to the sky. Imagine light is pouring into the mouth of this funnel. You are opening your seventh chakra.

5.   When you sit down and get ready to do the exercise below, put your hand on your heart and feel all your love and longing for your baby. This will open your fourth chakra.

Now that your chakras are open, you are ready for the following conversation with your baby, or for the exercise in connecting with his guides. If you want, you can combine the two exercises, connecting first with your baby, then with his guides. Or you may want to try the two exercises at two different times.

☙

Exercise to Ask Your Baby About Life Purpose

1.   Do the grounding exercise and make sure you feel connected to the earth.

2.   If you are connecting with an energetic baby (preconception), connect to your baby using the cord from your heart, or just by sensing in the room where your baby is. If you want, you can imagine you are holding that energetic baby in your arms.

If you are connecting with a physical baby in the

womb, place your hands on your belly and imagine they are sinking into the womb until they are gently holding your baby.

3.   As always, take a few minutes to breathe and enjoy being with your baby. Gently open to feeling your baby's energy. Notice if your baby's energy feels the same as the last time you did this exercise, or different. After all, if physical, this baby is growing and changing tremendously every day. And, just like you, your baby may have different moods on different days. Your baby and your connection to your baby may also be affected by your continuing conversation together, whether the baby is energetically in your field or already in the physical. The baby may begin to feel closer to you and more comfortable with coming into the physical.

4.   Greet your baby and send him all your love. Listen/ sense/ look for his response, depending on how you perceive him.

5.   Start by asking a simple, open-ended question. *How are you feeling today? Do you have anything you want to tell me today?* If you are trying the journaling technique for the first time, this would be a good time to begin writing down your baby's responses. If you are not journaling, just pay attention to anything you feel coming from your baby.

6.   Tell your baby you want to do your very best to help him incarnate and set a good foundation for his life. Let him know it would help you to know if he has a life purpose, a reason for coming to this life in this time to these parents. Ask him if he would share this life purpose, or mission, with you. Listen in whatever way you do, or try journaling the answer.

7.   Ask your baby any questions you may have about this life purpose, or about anything else that's on your mind.

8. Before you end the exercise, be sure you take some more time just to enjoy your baby's energy. End the conversation with a tender "good-bye for now."

If you were able to hear or write an answer, or feel it at an intuitive level, congratulations. You now have some valuable information to help you raise your child.

If you were not able to write anything that made sense, or hear or feel anything helpful, don't worry. Please keep practicing and trying. And remember, it is not that important that you get specific information from your baby. What's important is the love you demonstrate by taking time to spend with your baby

You are also welcome to contact me at www.motherbabytalk.com if you want advice or help with these methods.

Exercise to Connect with Your Baby's Guides

This exercise will be much easier if you are well grounded and if you do the exercise to open your chakras.

1. As always, find a comfortable place to sit and do your grounding exercise.

2. Feeling that connection with the earth through the lines of light coming from your feet, set your intention to connect with your baby's guide or guides.

3. Now just let your attention go out into the room. If you had to say where you felt this guide or guides were, where would you say they were? Don't think, just go with what you feel.

4. Wherever you think you feel a presence, let yourself be drawn to that energy. What does it feel like? What

kind of vibration do you feel? Is it a large presence, or not so large? Does it feel calm or excited? What's the energy of this being? Take a moment just to feel the energy, get a picture, or connect in whatever way works for you.

5.   Greet the presence and ask if you are connecting with your baby's guides. If you feel a "yes" current, great. If you feel a "no" current, you can ask who this being is, or you can ask "yes" or "no" questions. You might ask if this being is your guide, or the energetic presence of someone you know. (If you have been thinking a lot about a relative or friend, it is possible that person may be in your field energetically.)

If you find you are connecting with some other being—your guide, for example, you might want to try dialoguing with that being, since that's who you have connected with easily. After all, your guide may also know the answers to your questions about your baby, as well as your own life. You can ask about your own life purpose.

6.   If you feel you have managed to connect with your baby's guide, just take a moments to be with that presence. This is the bigger self of your baby. This is really the being you are incarnating, more even than the sweet little baby. It can be an awesome and life-changing experience to feel the bigger picture, to see who your child really is. (Wait a minute, you may be thinking. I thought you said this was my child's spirit guide? Well, there are no definitive dictionaries on this realm. What I felt when I found this presence was that it was my child, in his bigger self. After he was born and began to truly ground into his physical body, this bigger self was still there to guide and protect him, as a spirit guide.)

7.   Ask this being any questions you may have. You can ask open-ended questions, or "yes" or "no" questions.

You can feel or listen for a response, or write the answers in your journal. Here are some questions you might want to ask:

What is my baby's life purpose?

Can I do anything to facilitate this mission?

Why did my baby choose me/us as parents?

Do you have any advice for conceiving this baby?

Do I need to do anything particular to help my baby be healthy right now?

How can I best help my baby ground into his physical body?

What do I need to know about raising my baby?

Is there anything that would help me to know about guiding my child's different stages of life: Infancy? Toddlerhood? Preschool days? Starting school? Elementary school days? Middle school/early adolescence? High school/teenage years? Young adulthood?

Are there any issues between us from past lives when we might have known each other that need resolving or that we need to let go of?

These questions are just ideas, of course. Please ask whatever is in your heart to ask.

8.   As you bring this conversation to a close, thank the being and take a moment to honor this presence that is a larger part of your baby. Say "good-bye for now" and bring the conversation to a close.

If you were not journaling, take time to write down what you learned right away. You may not remember it very well later. Remember you can consult this being at any time, before and after conception and birth, even as the child grows up, for advice on raising your unique child.

Chapter Six

PREPARING TO BE
A MOTHER

*W*hat's it like being a mother? Can I be a mother? How
do I do that? Will I be good enough? Will I try *too* hard? Will
I do all the same things my mother did? Do I want to do
that?

If you are awaiting your first child, these are some of the
questions you may be asking yourself. Some women don't
start thinking about these questions until they are pregnant.
Others need to work on their issues with motherhood before
they are ready to conceive.

No other relationship affects us as much as our relationship
with our mother. When we are born, that relationship spells
life and death for us—physically and emotionally. The
emotional aspect is as important as the physical aspect.
If a child is fed by one person, but loved and cuddled by
another, the baby will bond with the person who loves and
cuddles her. If a baby is fed but not touched and caressed,
the child may stop growing.

On that first relationship we base all our subsequent
relationships. Of course, our relationships, particularly
with men, will also be based on our relationships with our
father, or whoever takes the role of father-figure in our lives.
But the power of that first all-consuming relationship with

the mother is never again duplicated—until we have our
own children. Even then, keep in mind, the relationship is
not the same, is not equal, nor ever will be. Even though
your children may seem to disregard you when they are
teenagers, when they are babies, you are their whole world.
When they are in the womb, you are *literally* their whole
world. Your cells surround them, your sounds fill their ears,
they drink your bodily fluids. They swim inside you, and
you fill them with the love and nourishment that is life. That
kind of all encompassing relationship continues for the first
several years after birth. For the first years of life, you are
the ground they stand on. If you are there when they need
you, but let them venture out when they are ready, they will
eventually learn to find their ground in the wider world,
with a whole range of relationships to support them.

I always think how strange it is that we receive absolutely
no formal training in being parents, the most important job
we will ever have. Of course, what use would it be to give
parenting classes to teenagers or college students? Most of
them would not be interested until they are getting ready to
have their own children (except perhaps the ones who are
becoming parents at that time). I fantasize that such a class
could be taught in a way that would teach young people
about themselves and their own relationship with their own
parents, but I don't see that going into any curriculum any
time soon. Too bad, because all of us could use that kind
of support and knowledge, both as young people and as
prospective parents.

I remember when my son was born. I remember feeling for
the first six or seven weeks of his life that I had absolutely no
idea what I was doing. After a couple of months, I realized
that nobody knew more about this particular baby than I
did, and that every mother is just making it up as she goes
along. That helped me feel much more comfortable with my
level of expertise as a mother.

Of course, there are degrees of knowledge. If you have

helped raise younger siblings, or have worked as a nanny or daycare provider, you may know much more than I did when my son was born.

In some parts of the world today, and in some households in this country, several generations live in the same household, and the older generation is around to help, model, and advise. I remember a Chinese friend telling me that, when his first child was born, his mother and father did almost all the childcare, and he and his wife really didn't need to know anything. If you have a close and healthy relationship with your parents, and they live in the same house, or at least the same town, they will be able to support you, if they are so inclined.

But many of us face a different reality. Our parents live in another town, perhaps on another coast or even in another country. We live in a single-family dwelling, much more isolated than our ancient tribal ancestors, when there was always another adult or an older child on hand to help. We may or may not feel comfortable with the way our parents raised us. We may or may not have an elder sister or aunt-type person in our lives to advise us. We are all, as I realized as a first-time mother, making it up as we go along.

What are your feelings about being a mother? How do you feel about yourself in this arena? I have a good friend who assured me she would never have children, because she was afraid she would be just like her mother, who suffered from severe depression. I was a little incredulous. I was sure she would be a good mother. Fifteen years later, I am happy to report she is a marvelous mother to a little girl and boy, and does not even remember making this statement to me.

There is a whole range of reasons why you might wonder about your parenting skills. You may have had parents who were alcoholics or mentally ill. You may have experienced emotional, verbal, physical, or sexual abuse as a child. You may have been raised by grandparents and never known your real parents. You may have been adopted, and have a whole range of feelings about that. Or you may, like me, have parents who were decent people, who did the best they could, but had their own emotional baggage to deal with, which of course affected me and my brother. We all do that to our children to some extent. What my husband and I strive to do is to heal our own wounds as much as possible, and to be conscious, as much as we can, of our emotions and patterns and beliefs, and how they affect us as parents, and affect our children.

If you have emotional baggage to deal with, if you have been abused in some way and never talked about it, and you want to have children, now is the time to get help. All of us, even those who seem to have had happy-go-lucky childhoods, generally have some emotional issue that we are working to heal. The best way to help your children is to help yourself. I highly recommend working with a therapist or energy healer to work out any issues you feel may affect you as a parent. In my experience the best way to do this is to work with a therapist who can help you repattern your neurosystem through EMDR (Eye Movement Desensitization and Reprocessing) or neurofeedback, while at the same time working with a well-trained energy healer. A Barbara Brennan Healing Science Practitioner such as myself helps clients release old patterns and heal past trauma that is locked into the human energy field, which includes your physical, emotional, mental, and spiritual bodies. This combination of neuro-repatterning therapy and energy work has been highly successful for many of my clients, including those who suffered severe trauma as children. To find a Barbara Brennan practitioner in your area, check out www.barbarabrennan.com and look for "Find a Graduate." (If you are in the U.S., look under the information for the U.S. school. If in Europe, try the info on the school in Europe.) You may also contact me for distance healings. To find a practitioner in your town who uses

EMDR, go to www.emdr.com and search on "Find an EMDR Clinician."

It may be that your childhood was not traumatic, but you still have worries and concerns about being a mother. Often I find that women who go on to be great mothers have a lot of anxiety about their motherhood just before they become first-time mothers. Talking with your baby about these concerns can put these issues in a different light.

Lisa, the 41-year-old family law attorney, was worried about being too controlling, as her own mother was. She told her baby about her fears. "She told me that we all had lessons and she knew we'd be the perfect parents. She trusted me to protect her, and parent her appropriately. She reminded me that energy was pure, and if I felt stuck, go back to that place."

One of my first clients had been severely physically abused by her father. She was angry at her mother for not protecting her. At the same time, her mother had been depressed and angry over her husband's affairs, so my client ended up taking care of her mother. A major issue for her, as she was trying to conceive, was her relationship with her mother. She finally was able to articulate that she would feel afraid to leave a child of hers alone with her mother, yet she would want her mother's help with her baby. She had a deep longing to connect with her mother, yet felt unable to trust her totally. During a Mother-Baby Bonding Session with me, she came to understand that it was okay for her to set a clear boundary with her mother, that being connected to her mother did not mean surrendering her own sense of herself, or feeling compelled to do anything that did not ring true for her.

One of my clients, who experienced sexual abuse as a child, received a clear message from her father that she was more useful as a sexual object than as a woman. She remembers how much her parents hated each other and how she took that hatred and turned it into hatred against herself and her womanhood, particularly her womb. When she wanted to become a mother, she had to learn to look at her hidden beliefs—beliefs such as "Men are scary."

Her baby actually helped her with this process in a Mother-Baby Bonding session. He helped her see that her beliefs were limiting her ability to conceive. He also showed her that her fears of what kind of mother she would be were overblown.

While I was writing my senior thesis, I interviewed a woman I will call Amy, who was an artist and mother of two girls. Amy was born in 1959 and grew up hearing a lot about the atomic bomb and pollution. "There was this incredible geyser of information about how messed up the world was. Why would you bring any kids into this world?" Despite the fact that she grew up in a big Italian family "with people having kids all over the place," the message she got was fear, and that world conditions made it "an incredible crime to have a child."

One day while pregnant with her second daughter, Amy was meditating next to a creek. She had "this incredible desire to stop being motivated by fear," she remembered. After lying by the creek for a long time, she said, "It was like my fear was exhausted by prayer." She finally let go of her fear and "calm flushed through." She kept getting the message that this pregnancy "wasn't for myself." She explained, "I wasn't in control. I was serving by having this baby."

The important thing to remember is that this baby chose you. She chose you because you are perfect for her to learn whatever it is she needs to learn in this world. That doesn't mean just what you can teach her intentionally. It also means that whatever healing she hopes to accomplish in this lifetime will be jumpstarted by being your child. Your love, your tenderness, your ability to parent will nurture her. And your unique qualities, whatever they are, will be the roadmap that allows her to find the path to her own personal growth and healing in this lifetime. If you don't believe me, ask your baby!

❦

Exercise to Prepare for Being a Mother

1. Sit comfortably with both feet on the ground. Take a few deep breaths, and ground your feet into the ground. Imagine those lines of light going from your feet down through the floor, through the foundation of the house, into the soil, through the bedrock, and deep into the earth, where they connect with the iron and nickel core of the earth.

2. Feel and breathe your connection to the earth. Feel your energy dropping down into your feet and the softness of the earth holding you. Let go of any stress or tension you feel in your body.

3. Let yourself connect with your baby through your heart and, if you are pregnant, through your hands.

4. As always, greet your baby, send your love and try to feel her response.

5. If you have been practicing journaling as a way of receiving answers to your questions, this would be a good time to try that.

6. Take time to tell your baby how you are feeling about becoming a mother. Include all your feelings— excitement, joy, apprehension, fear—whatever they are. Explain in detail how you are feeling and why. If you have fears and doubts about being a mother, explain to the baby where those fears and doubts come from, and how you are working with them. Be sure to also explain in detail to the baby all your wonderful feelings of

anticipation and joy at becoming a mother to this baby.

7.   Then listen for a response. Again, that response may be in the form of words, or it may just be sensations. Pay attention to every little nuance that you detect.

8.   If you have found that you can detect a yes or no current from your baby, try asking some yes and no questions about your concerns about being a mother.

9.   Make sure you finish your session with a tender good-bye to your baby. If you were not journaling during the session, take a minute now to write down your impressions from this session. You may want to take some extra time to journal for yourself how you are feeling about becoming a mother and to explore those feelings through your journal. Sometimes through writing we discover feelings or make connections in ways we would not otherwise.

Chapter Seven

TAKING CARE OF YOURSELF AND YOUR BABY DURING PREGNANCY

*N*estled in your womb, your baby is growing, forming cells, building the blocks that will make his body, his will, his emotions, his life. Most of the blue print for how he will face life—his reactions, his characteristics, his ability to face the future, his understanding of how the world around him works—is being formed right now. This time is so important and precious, because it is our beliefs, more than anything else, that form our future, our past and our present.

What does your baby believe about life? This depends in part on his genetic make-up and, I believe, his past life experiences. While you may or may not believe in past lives, we can probably agree that his experiences throughout this lifetime will form a large part of his character and expectations for life. A significant contribution to your baby's personality and belief system—for pre- and perinatal psychologists, the key ingredient—will be his experience in the womb. If he is being carried softly and lovingly, then softness and love will be his expectation and his experience of life. If he feels his mother grounded in her body, and connecting to him, then it will be easier for him to ground into his newly forming body, and to connect with himself and others.

What kind of atmosphere can you make for yourself that will ease your pregnancy and help your baby get the best start in life?

The most important thing you can do, as we noted in Chapter Two, is learn as much as you can about your own emotions, your own reactions and your own belief systems. The more you know about how you react to life—your own unconscious—the more you will be free to respond to events and build your life from your center, your true being, rather than your patterns and reactions. What a gift to give to your baby! What an example to set for him!

Nowhere do these patterns come out more than in our intimate relationships. What kind of a relationship do you have with your partner or the father of this baby? Many people make the mistake of thinking a baby will improve their relationship with their partner, that it will be a bridge between them to heal any rifts. Be wary of this kind of thinking! Nothing tests a relationship like the arrival of a new baby. Roles shift, patterns you have never seen before will rise up like whales beaching on the shore. These new patterns will be patterns set in you during your own time in the womb and your babyhood—ways of relating to your partner, your child, your life, set in you by your parents' example. Only by hard work and conscious evaluation of yourself will you be able to sort through these patterns and see them for what they are. And the first few days and months of your child's life may not be the best time for this process.

If anything is not smooth in your relationship with your partner now, it may only be magnified by the arrival of a child, not solved. If you have anything you need to clear up and improve between you and your partner, do it now, *before* the baby arrives in your arms. Then you will have a solid base on which to build a family.

Physically, you may have some unique needs, but much is universal. Adequate sleep, exercise, as little stress as possible, abstinence from any drugs (including alcohol and cigarettes), vitamins and minerals, especially calcium to form bones and folic acid to prevent birth defects—you know about all of this. Avoid coffee if you can. Caffeine is a drug as well, and will definitely affect your baby's nervous system.

In terms of stress, try to avoid moving (as in changing houses or locations) during pregnancy. Moving is one of the most stressful events in our lives. It's better to move before you get pregnant, or even after the baby arrives, believe it or not. If you absolutely cannot avoid it, try to make the move as stress-free as possible. (Talk to the baby about it and your feelings about it. This will make it easier for him—and you!)

We talked in Chapter Four about ultrasound and how it can damage chromosomes and breakdown DNA. Nevertheless, most women do choose to have ultrasounds. If you are an older mother, or have a history of birth defects in your family, you may feel it's important to do an ultrasound. In this case, make sure you prepare the baby for the procedure by talking to him about it beforehand—and check in with him afterwards to see how he is doing. If you want, you could even try to connect with him during the procedure.

The decision to have an amniocentesis is also a personal one. This procedure in particular is quite invasive to the developing fetus. Researchers used ultrasound to see how babies reacted to amniocentesis. They discovered repeatedly that babies will bat a needle away or move away from it during amniocenteses. There seems no doubt that they feel threatened by this procedure.[1]

When Lisa decided to have an amniocentesis, both she and her healer talked to the baby beforehand. They explained what would happen and told the baby there would still be plenty of fluid in the womb. "We told the baby that we still

[1] Emerson, William, The Vulnerable Prenate, *Pre and Perinatal Psychology Journal*, 10(3), Spring 1996, p. 126-127.

love you and want you," Lisa said. She talked to her own guides and felt calm and prepared going into the procedure.

Nevertheless, the amniocentesis was a traumatic experience, both for her and her child. For Lisa, the procedure brought back memories and feelings from two previous abortions. At the moment the uterus was punctured, Lisa felt energy draining out of the uterus along with the fluid. She felt the baby "rip the energy out." The baby got very agitated, kicking and rolling around. "She got so upset," Lisa said.

Afraid of miscarriage, Lisa pulled her own energy up, losing her grounding. Fortunately, she had her healer and her Barbara Brennan skills to help her. At her next healing, the healer spent a half an hour working on the baby. Lisa felt the energy start to seep back into the uterus. The healer and Lisa herself also did energetic work to heal the uterus.

An amniocentesis may not bring back the same memories for you—it may be a much calmer experience. If you stay calm, it will help the baby. If you choose to do an amniocentesis, do take a session or two communicating with your baby to explain this procedure and prepare the baby. If he knows and understands what is happening, it will be easier for him.

When I was pregnant, I did none of these tests, but I was working on a computer at work for several hours a day. I was quite concerned about how this was affecting the baby, knowing as I did that the electromagnetic field of a computer "eats up" the energy field of a human adult. What would it do to a growing vulnerable prenate? I ordered a lead apron from an office equipment magazine, similar to the kind used during X-rays, but actually made for pregnant women using a computer, to wear while I was working.

I found that my baby often told me, without words, but nonverbally, what he wanted. If I had been working for too long at the computer without taking a break, he would begin to kick. I would get up and take a walk around the building, breathing deeply, and he would calm down. Likewise if I stayed up late reading and needed to go to bed, he would protest by kicking. Once I stopped reading and went to bed, he would calm down.

Your baby may communicate similarly with kicks and jabs. But you can also check in with your baby during your Mother-Baby Bonding sessions and ask what he needs—and what he thinks you need—during this time.

Remember, even if you do not hear words from your baby, you can still get answers to questions like this. I remember one mother who asked her baby what she needed during her pregnancy. She did not hear the baby, but she saw colors in response her questions. When she asked what she needed to care for herself and her baby, I heard the baby say she needed to eat a lot of leafy green vegetables, particularly a lot of salad. The mother saw the color green.

I would like to recommend one tool that helped me tremendously during pregnancy and particularly during childbirth. The Monroe Institute's *Opening the Way for Pregnancy and Childbirth,* available as a series of cassette tapes or a digital download, is a wonderful way to ease your pregnancy and aid your labor and delivery. I cannot recommend it enough. As I will explain in Chapter 11, it took hours off my labor.

The Monroe Institute is a center in Faber, Virginia, 30 minutes south of Charlottesville, Virginia, where people come from all over the world to learn about Hemi-Sync, a method developed by Robert Monroe of using brain waves to access one's higher self. The *Opening the Way* series was developed in concert with a midwife and with the special needs of a mother—during pregnancy, childbirth and after birth—in mind. There is even one part for "Connecting with the Soul of Your Baby," which is different from the method used in this book, but may help you develop the energetic connection with your baby. You can order *Opening the Way* from www.hemi-sync.com and find more information on the

Monroe Institute from www.monroeinstitute.org. The best way to use this series is with headphones, so you access both sides of the brain directly.

Another product you might consider ordering from the Monroe Institute is the *Catnapper Album*. This product allows you to take a 30-minute nap (it helps put you to sleep) that feels like a 90-minute nap. I found this product invaluable once my baby was born and I needed to be able to nap during the day. But it could also be helpful to keep you rested during pregnancy.

Next time you do a session with your baby, ask him what he needs—and what he thinks you need—for a healthy, successful pregnancy.

Chapter Eight
PREPARING FOR BIRTH

*B*eing pregnant can be a wonderful experience, or a difficult experience. One thing is certain—it does end. And at the end of pregnancy comes that passage called birth.

Birth is one of the most exciting, wonderful, transformative moments in a woman's life.

But I have found that many women, even those who feel comfortable with the idea of becoming a mother, have many fears and doubts about giving birth. One way to alleviate these fears is talk to your baby.

Your baby may know more than you about what is going to happen at the birth, and may be able to give you some tips for preparation. Ask your baby what she needs to feel comfortable at birth, and whether there is anything she thinks you need to know about the delivery.

Danielle remembers that the day before her daughter's birth, "I was clearly instructed to put a large towel between my legs when I went to bed." This seemed odd to her, because her due date was a week away, and she planned to deliver by C-section because her body is small and her baby was big. Sure enough, however, at 5 o'clock the next morning, her water broke and the towel caught the first "gush." She delivered her baby by C-section about noon.

Amy, an artist and mother of two girls, was pregnant with her first daughter when she had this experience. The baby was two weeks late, and Amy was feeling stressed about the impending birth. She went for a walk in a beautiful old-growth forest near her home and sat down to meditate. "It felt like a very large, luminous angel was putting her hand on my head to (get me to) relax, trust....a very comforting gesture." The angel told Amy, "I was going to have a little girl and everything was going to be all right."

Amy had been rather agitated about the baby arriving late. But after this experience, she said, "I just had this inner smile. I had this sense of peace." She was planning to have her baby at home. "I really trusted I was doing it the way it needed to be done. I was so happy because I really wanted a girl. I remember skipping home, really happy." She felt this experience of letting go was very calming to her uterus. She went into labor the next day, and the baby was born the following day.

Talk to your baby about your preparations for birth. Explain where the birth is going to be and what is going to happen. Don't hesitate to ask your baby for her input—does she have a preference about where she will be born, or with whom? If you are working through any fears about delivery, be sure to connect to your baby and explain your fears and how you are working with them. If you have strong fears about labor and delivery and are trying to conceive, your energetic baby—though not yet conceived—may have helpful insights for you.

Lisa, the family law attorney, told her baby about the birth, what to expect and who would be there. The baby responded by getting "excited," Lisa wrote in her journal. "I saw her core star start to stand out and pulse brightly.... It was so beautiful. She became more active, kicking and moving. I told her what a delight it was to feel this. I asked her if she had any needs. She said, "Just you." She then said she appreciated the reassurance I gave her.

There are many good books about preparing for labor, so we will not go into too much detail here. I would just like to talk about the issue of who is at your delivery. Remember that you need to feel comfortable and supported by whomever is at your birth. Choose a doctor or midwife whom you trust and feel comfortable with. If you have a doctor, you might think about having a doula who would support you for the entire labor.

Your style is unique. Do you want to have a lot of people at your birth, or just you and your partner? I planned to have a good friend come, but in the end, it was just me, my husband, my midwife and her nurse. That worked for me, because I turned out to need space and silence to concentrate. My best friend, on the other hand, had about 10 people at her first birth, including her mother and numerous friends.

Some women like to have their mothers present. Be careful, however, to create an atmosphere that pleases you, not other people. If there were ever a time to think first about yourself, this is it. If your mother lives close enough and wants to come and you would feel more comfortable with her there, this is a wonderful time for the two of you to share. If, however, there are issues between you and your mother, don't be afraid to say what you want. I remember one midwife telling me how she noticed her client's labor would come to a stop every time her mother came in the room. When her mother left the room, her labor would start back up. The midwife finally had to ask the mother to stay out of the delivery room, in order for the delivery to be completed.

One woman I know, a social worker and mother of three sons, chose not to have her mother present at her first delivery, but was surprised to find that during contractions she called out for her mother. "While I was in labor, I was a loud person," she remembered. "I called for my mother the whole time."

She did the same thing during the births of her second and third children, even though by that time her mother had passed away. "It was sort of calling out to the Great Mother," she recalled. "I can't tell you that it was actually in my head that I was calling for my mother, but she was the one who always comforted me."

Labor and delivery are as individual as personality. One woman's experience may be totally different from another's. Some women labor for three hours, others for 36. What your labor will be like, no one knows. However, there are some clues. If this is your second child, you have some idea of your body's rhythms in birth. Beware, though, of assuming all will be the same the second time. My friend, an engineering professor, learned this the hard way. Her first child, a boy, arrived three weeks late. When she became pregnant with her second child, she assumed her daughter would also arrive late. When the baby was born three weeks early, she was caught unprepared.

My midwife used to say, "After three babies, we'll know your pattern for birthing a baby." But, she said, "since you'll be finished by then or before then, we'll never really know." However, she used to add, even a first-time mother can get a good idea of what her pattern might be by talking with her mother. Often a women's experience in pregnancy and delivery will be similar to her mother's.

I find that many women have never talked to their mothers about their pregnancies or delivery experiences. If you are pregnant, or thinking about getting pregnant, and your mother is alive and on good terms with you, take some time to ask her what her pregnancy and delivery were like. Did she find being pregnant easy or difficult? Did she experience much morning sickness? During which trimester did she feel most tired? How were her spirits? Did she experience any bleeding? Were there any complications during the pregnancy?

Take into account, of course, your age at pregnancy and your mother's age. If they were very different, that can affect the pregnancy. And you are a different person from your mother, so your pattern may be different from hers. But they are often similar.

Knowing my mother's pattern during pregnancy and delivery was very helpful to me. Although our ages were different (my mother was 28 during her first pregnancy, I was 36), our pregnancies and deliveries were remarkably similar. She often felt uncomfortable, but was never actually sick during her pregnancies. I was the same. She went into labor in the evening, but did not have her babies until the middle of the night after the following day. I followed the same pattern, except I was able to deliver my son much earlier, thanks to the Monroe tapes which I discussed in Chapter Seven.

Ask your mother detailed questions about her labor and delivery. What time of day did she go into labor? How long was she in labor? Did she deliver vaginally or by C-section? Did she use any drugs, or was her labor natural? What did she find easy about labor? What did she find difficult?

Take some time, of course, for her to tell you (again, perhaps) how she felt when she first saw you and held you. Make sure you also know what happened to you at birth. Did you stay with your mother? Where there complications that affected you or her? Were you separated for any length of time?

As a healer, I have found that one of the most wounding episodes in life is separation from the mother at birth. In hospitals babies have been routinely separated from their mothers and put to sleep in nurseries, far from their mothers' sides. That is beginning to change. Many hospitals now keep babies in a crib in their mother's room, rather than placing them in a nursery.

Of course, there are times when medical emergencies dictate that mother and child must be separated for some length of time. In these cases, the presence of the father is so important. As long as the baby is in the father's arms, or close enough to the father to feel his energy field and his loving presence, the impact of separation from the mother will be greatly reduced.

If you were separated from your mother at birth, it may not only affect your outlook on life and your relationships, but it may also have an impact on your feelings about giving birth yourself. I personally chose not to give birth in a hospital. Because of my own wounding at being separated from my mother at birth, just entering the labor and delivery ward in the hospital was enough to send me into panic. I decided to give birth in a birth center with a midwife.

Even if your own experience of birth was a good one, you may have many questions, fears and doubts about delivering a baby. Take advantage of the many classes offered for birth preparation. I recommend the Bradley method classes. These classes prepare you for childbirth while allowing for differences between individual women.

Talk to your women friends and relatives about their birth experiences. Get an idea of the wide range of experiences and the wide range of what's normal. Beware of talking with anyone who is holding her own fear about birth. Remember that birth is a natural, normal experience, and that your feelings about your labor and delivery are very important. Giving birth to a baby is very much affected by your psyche. If you feel calm and supported, you will have a much different experience, both emotionally and physically, than if you feel anxious or afraid.

Sometimes fears of giving birth can even create blocks to conception. When I do a healing or Mother Baby Bonding session with these clients, we often find a past life in which the mother or the baby or both died during childbirth.

Until very recently in human history, complications during delivery was the leading cause of death among young women. So the chance of us having traumatic past life experiences with birth is extremely high.

I myself had a lot of fear about giving birth before my son was born. Before I became pregnant I gave myself a healing in which I "birthed" a baby that was energetically still inside my body. It seemed that both the baby and I had died at birth.

Despite this healing and the fact that I worked on my fears before I became pregnant, I was still carrying some fears about delivery seven months into my pregnancy. I realized this because my baby told me. I was at the Monroe Institute doing the Gateway introductory program. One afternoon while I was resting, I made contact with my baby and asked him to go head down in preparation for delivery.

The baby quickly replied that he didn't want to do any such thing. There was too much fear in my pelvis and it made him just want to go away, he said. He certainly didn't want to go head down into it. It was too scary. At that point I worked on feeling the fear in my pelvis, giving myself a healing response, and releasing the fear, which I was able to do.

The following weekend the baby went head down in position for birth and stayed that way until the delivery. At my next checkup my midwife commented that the baby was in an excellent position. I was grateful for this exchange at the Monroe Institute. I am sure it made my delivery much easier, and possibly averted a trip to the hospital for a Cesarean section, since my midwife would not have delivered a breech baby.

If you feel you are carrying fear about giving birth, try to find a good healer, such as a Certified Brennan Healing Science Practitioner, who can help you clear any past life trauma, or whatever is creating fear in your system. You can also try the exercise at the end of this chapter, which may help you identify and release your fear. I am also available to talk with you and work with you over the telephone or through a long-distance healing.

᠗

Exercise for Preparing for Birth and Clearing Fears About Birth

1. Sitting comfortably with your feet on the floor, ground your feet down into the floor, and send those lines of light from your feet deep into the earth. Feel your energy settling into your feet.

2. Now imagine those two lines of light, one from each foot, going up through your legs, meeting in your pelvis and continuing as one line of light up through your torso, right through your heart, up through your neck and head and out the top of your head, up towards the sky. Feel yourself connected to both the sky and the earth, yourself the bridge between.

3. Breathe and feel your first chakra reaching from your pelvic floor all the way down to the earth. Feel your seventh chakra opening to the sky from the top of your head.

4. Let the energy of the earth and the energy of the sky come into your body and meet in the fire of your heart.

5. From that place in your heart, let yourself feel whatever you feel about the impending birth. Take time to feel each feeling one by one. If you are feeling excitement, let yourself feel that in all of its fullness. If you are feeling joy, let that come fully into your heart and savor it. If you are feeling fear, let yourself feel that, and voice out loud any fears you have about giving birth. No fear is too silly or too unreasonable. Hold a space for yourself to really feel those fears, cry about them if you need to. If you want to, you can write them down. Let yourself feel deeply into each fear. See what other concern or fear may be behind the initial fear. Spend time to really look at each concern and let it be held in the fire

of your heart. Imagine each of these fears is a frightened child, and simply hold it the way you would hold such a child.

6. If you do this process thoroughly (it may take more than one session), you may find these fears clear one by one.

7. Whatever you are feeling, take some time to talk to your baby about the impending birth. Start by explaining to the baby everything you know about the birth—where it will be, who will be there, who will be holding the space for both of you, physically and emotionally.

8. Tell your baby what you are feeling—excitement about seeing her, looking forward to holding her.

9. Ask if there is anything you need to know to help her through the birth process. Ask if she knows anything about what is going to happen during the birth. Is there anything you need to know to help yourself?

10. Then, if you have any fears, you can explain that you have certain fears about giving birth, but they are your fears, and you are working through them. Ask the baby if she has anything she wants to share about those fears—how they are affecting her, or what she has to say about them. (By the way, just to be clear, this is NOT a process you would do with a child already out of the womb. You might explain to a child that you have certain fears if they are affecting your behavior toward that child. But you would not ask a child to help you deal with your own fears. Another adult is the appropriate person to go to. You don't want to ask a child to handle adult fears. But at this stage of his life, your baby—whether in the womb or before conception—is still connected to sources of wisdom that go far beyond the conscious human realm. Still, be clear that you are the one holding a space for your fears and concerns, and that you will get professional help if need be. In this case, you are simply

being open and clear with your baby about how you are really feeling. And since she may at this stage know more than you about what is going to happen, you are simply consulting with her, but not asking her to carry the weight of your feelings.)

11. Again, this conversation will happen at whatever level of communication is possible for you. If not in words, you may still find that you receive wordless, but very clear assurance from the baby that everything will be fine—or you may get a sense without words of what the baby needs from you to be prepared for the birth.

12. If you find you are unable to clear your fears and concerns by yourself, please do contact me at www.motherbabytalk.com to set up a session, or look for a Barbara Brennan healer in your local area at www.barbarabrennan.com. Not all healers specialize in this area as I do, but any competent healer should be able to help you clear these kinds of concerns from your energy field.

13. After you are finished talking with your baby, make sure you close your session with her, and thank her for her participation in this process.

Chapter Nine

Dad Talks with His Baby: A Chapter for Fathers, Partners and Adoptive Parents

$\mathcal{J}$ust as an energy cord connects the heart of the mother and her baby, so a similar energy cord connects the father and his baby. This cord needs to be strong and full of light and love for all to go well with the baby, his mother and his father.

While the role of the father is different from that of the mother, it is just as crucial and necessary for the life of a child. Obviously, it is just as biologically necessary, but energetically and emotionally a child without a father will have an incomplete experience of life.

Of course, another person may take the role of father and fill this role admirably. In these days of adoption, gay marriage, artificial insemination and surrogate mothers, the parents of a baby may or may not be the baby's biological parents. Whoever takes it upon themselves to love and raise a child becomes his parents, emotionally, psychologically and energetically.

This chapter is written for fathers, for partners and for anyone who has taken it upon themselves to parent a child, be that child related to you biologically or not. You may do these exercises with a child who is not yet conceived or is in the womb—if you are hoping to adopt or have a surrogate mother, for example.

As a father or partner, you have a special role in the life of a child. Mothers and children often form very tight bonds of mutual nurturing and comfort. Your role is to support that circle of love, but also to allow the child to break out of that circle and experience the wider world. Your job is to invite the child to explore, to navigate unchartered waters—and to be the companion in that adventure. Thus do you teach your child that anything is possible, if aided by love.

Obviously, your job, especially in the beginning, is also to support your wife or partner as she goes through the incredible experience of bearing, birthing and giving life to a baby. No other experience in life so changes and marks a woman. You are her main support in this process. How you relate to her and to the baby will make a fundamental difference in your baby's permanent outlook on life.

Researchers of prenatal factors that affect a baby's health have ranked the quality of a mother's relationship with her husband or partner as the second most important aspect of the baby's emotional, mental and physical development. (The number one factor, as we discussed in Chapter Two, is how the mother feels about her baby.) One researcher, Dr. Dennis Scott, who studied over 1,300 children and their families, estimated that a woman locked in a stormy marriage runs a 237 percent greater risk of bearing a psychologically or physically damaged child than a woman in a secure, nurturing relationship. [1]

In lectures at the Barbara Brennan School, Brennan has said that the cord connections between the father and the baby must be strong for healthy conception and birth. Weaknesses in the energetic connections between the child

---

[1] Verny, Thomas, *The Secret Life of the Unborn Child* (Dell Publishing, 1981), p. 49.

and her father are sometimes a cause of miscarriage, she reports.[2] Like the fetal psychologists, Brennan says that she has realized lately that the role of the father is much more important than she had previously thought.

Nurturing this energetic connection can be more difficult for the husbands, or the partners of pregnant women, than the pregnant women themselves. First of all, they do not have the experience of carrying the baby in their bodies while the baby forms. Secondly, they cannot choose to experience the bonding process that occurs when a mother breastfeeds her baby. Since there are energetic chakras in the breasts, this experience not only represents a physical and emotional bond, it is also a powerful energetic exchange.

Nevertheless, the emotional and energetic connection between a father, or a partner, and a baby can be just as tight, just as close, as the relationship between mother and baby. How does this occur? The best way to start is to do the exercises below. A father or partner can do these exercises before conception or during pregnancy. You can even do them after the baby arrives, while holding the baby, or while you are away from the baby. Your connection with your child does not depend on space or time. It is infinite.

Don't be deceived by the fact that it is your wife or partner who bears, births and perhaps feeds the baby with her own body's resources. Your energy, your attitude toward life, your love for this baby is just as important as hers. Your role is different, but not any less crucial. You will notice this, as the baby grows. A child who does not spend time one-on-one with mother and with father, or with both partners, becomes unbalanced. It will be quite obvious to you when you spend time with your child that this time gives him a kind of balance, evenness, a joy in life, that nothing else does.

One final note: Occasionally it is the father, or partner, and

[2] Brennan, Barbara, School-wide lecture, Barbara Brennan School of Healing, 1999.

not the mother, who provides tenderness in a child's life. People are all different. If the mother does not emphasize that tenderness for her child that we normally call maternal, then the father will need to provide that tenderness with his love and attention. Occasionally the roles are reversed this way. Maybe the mother is a career woman, and the father is a stay-at-home dad. The children come to the father with their problems, and turn to the mother for their connection to the broader world. There is nothing wrong with this model. In fact, it is a wonderful example to other men, who so often have trouble accessing their tender side. If this is the case with you, we encourage you to acknowledge this fact and celebrate it. You have a special connection with your child. We honor your ability to hold that connection.

If you are planning to adopt a child, or have chosen a surrogate mother, you can connect with that child, whether the child has not yet been conceived, is *in u*tero, or has already been born. The process of connection, in any case, is not very different, though the energy of the baby may be different in those different phases.

⤫

Exercise to Connect with Your Child for Fathers, Partners and Adoptive Parents

You may do this exercise before the baby is conceived or while the baby is already growing in the womb. If you are waiting to adopt a child, you may also do this exercise after the child is born, but not yet with you. You don't necessarily need to know who the child is yet. Just set your intent to connect with the child who is coming to you.

Find a comfortable place to sit, where you can have both feet on the ground and sit fairly upright, but comfortably enough to sit still for some time.

   1.   Close your eyes and relax. Feel yourself sitting in the

chair. Feel the floor beneath your feet.

2.   Take three deep, slow breaths. Now imagine, as you continue relaxing, that all of your energy is sliding down through your body into your feet. Imagine that your feet are actually sinking into the floor.

3.   Now imagine there is a line of light going from the bottom of each of your feet into the floor.

4.   Imagine these lines of light sinking into floorboards, going through the rest of the house or building, and going into the soil.

5.   Let the lines of light go deep into the soil and connect with the bedrock of the earth. Imagine them going right through the bedrock, deep into the bowels of the earth. Let them connect with the viscous rock that lies deep in the mantle of the earth. See if you can feel the warmth of the viscous rock coming up to meet you.

6.   Finally, imagine these two lines of light connected to your feet actually penetrating the solid nickel core of earth. For a moment imagine yourself resting in the core of the earth, the same way a baby rests inside his mother. See if you can feel how the earth knows everything you need and supplies it in abundance.

7.   Place your hand on your heart and let your heart open. To help you with this, you can think about someone you love—your partner, your pet—whatever helps your heart open in its fullness. Now imagine there is a cord coming from deep in your heart that connects to your baby. Follow this cord to the place where it connects with your child.

8.   Another way of connecting with your baby is simply to ask yourself, if my child were somewhere near me, where would he be? Feel into the room around you and notice where you are drawn.

9. Whichever method you use, take some time now to sense into your baby. Simply breathe and connect with your baby's energy. Feel into your baby's energy. What is it like? How would you describe it? Light or dense? Soft or active? Buzzing? Quiet? Every baby is unique. What does this baby feel like to you?

10. Take a few moments to just breathe and be with your baby. See if you can attune yourself to your baby's energy and create even more connection between you.

11. When you are ready, send a message of greeting to your baby. What would you like to say to your energetic child? Let him know whatever is in your heart to say to him.

12. After sending a message to your energetic baby, take some time to see if you receive any kind of reply. This could be anything—a feeling of love, a picture in your mind, a sensation. You may even hear words— but you may not. Your reply may be something much more subtle—a vibration, a shift in the energy that you sense. If you practice this exercise regularly, these subtle vibrational responses may become clearer to you, and may develop into a kind of conversation, with or without words.

13. Before you ask specific questions of your child, you might want to just ask if the baby has anything to say or express to you. Feel into/listen carefully for the response. Again, it may be quite subtle. Pay attention to every sensation that you feel.

14. Now you may have some specific questions you want to ask. If you are receiving answers in sensations or vibrations, you may want to ask "yes" or "no" questions. Most of us can identify fairly easily the difference between a "yes" current and a "no" current. You might start by asking yourself a very simple question that you already know the answer to so you can feel the difference

between a "yes" and a "no" current in your body. For example, you might ask yourself, "Is my name Jackson?" or "Do I live in Miami?" Ask yourself a few "yes" or "no" questions so you get used to the feeling of these currents in your body.

15. What questions you ask will depend on your situation and your current relationship with the baby, but any prospective parent may want to ask about the personality of the child, tips on how to raise this child, etc. Ask whatever comes to your heart, to your mind, whatever you are curious about or need to know to connect with this child.

16. When you are ready to stop, let your baby know you are going to end the dialogue now, but you will take time for another chat in the near future. Take a moment to say good-bye, and let the child know you will connect again another time (if that indeed is your intention).

Take some time after your session to make a few notes of your experience and what you sensed. These records will be helpful as you develop your conversation with your child.

Congratulations! You have completed your first session communicating with your child. Celebrate whatever communication you feel occurred. If you feel you didn't sense much of anything, don't be discouraged. Learning to pay attention to subtle energy takes time and practice, just like anything else. Remember that, even if you feel like you are perceiving nothing at all, your child feels your intent to connect and your love, and that's the most important aspect of these sessions.

Chapter Ten

LOSING A BABY: CONVERSATIONS FOR MISCARRIAGE, STILLBIRTH OR ABORTION

*O*ne of the most difficult experiences a woman can go through is losing a baby through miscarriage or stillbirth. It is, first and foremost, a death. Archaeologists in Egypt have found mummies of fetuses in the Egyptian tombs, proof that in some cultures what we call a miscarriage or stillbirth was treated as a death equally deserving of a funeral and preparation for afterlife as any other.

Unfortunately, in our society, there is no ceremony and no structure to support that grief. These days the grief around miscarriages may be compounded by the fact that many mothers do not share the good news of their pregnancy until after the first trimester. This protects relatives from disappointment and prevents unnecessary explanations to friends, but it also isolates the mother who eventually experiences a miscarriage. Having been pregnant in secret, she is also then grieving in secret, not the best way to receive comfort and support.

I have always been ready to share the good news of my pregnancies as soon as I knew about them. I was never so grateful for that decision as when I miscarried my second child. Though it was difficult explaining to many people that I was no longer pregnant, the outpouring of support I received from the women around me was truly stunning. It seemed that nearly every woman I met had experienced her own miscarriage—a story she had never mentioned before, but which now came out willingly in my time of distress. These shared stories helped in a way no expression of sympathy could. I felt understood and not alone.

I was surprised to learn just how common miscarriage was. It turns out I know very few women who have not experienced a miscarriage. For some, it was a late and heavy period, before they were even sure they were pregnant. Others miscarried after several weeks, as I did, or even months. I was also surprised to learn—because I had never heard anyone talk about it—how physically difficult miscarriage can be. I talked to women who had bled heavily for weeks, or bled repeatedly.

I would like to encourage women to come out of the closet with their miscarriages. By keeping these experiences secret and private, we deprive ourselves of the support of other women like ourselves. We also fail to inform our daughters and friends, younger women in our lives, who may someday face the same experience.

Equally difficult is the situation of parents who have decided not to keep a fetus who has serious developmental problems, or the mother who has decided, for whatever reason, that the time is not right for her to have a child.

All of these parents can take advantage of the skills taught in this book to communicate with the child in question. When I knew that I might be miscarrying, one of the first things I did was to get in touch with the child. The baby assured me that we would be connected forever no matter what. This did not make my grief any less, but it offered a kind of comfort that nothing else could.

After the miscarriage, I felt the baby's energy body shift from my pelvic area to right in front my heart. I knew when the time came for me to get pregnant again, the baby would be waiting.

Still it took me several months before I was ready to connect with the baby again. What I felt and heard immediately was the baby's clear and constant love. "I love you," a little voice was saying. This reduced me to tears, and I was able to release the grief I had been holding on to. I also saw that I had in some way held myself responsible for the miscarriage. I felt as though, in losing the baby, I had somehow not been a good mother. It was good to see this, and release myself from this false belief.

I also discovered that I was literally preventing myself from getting pregnant again. Afraid of another miscarriage, and still carrying my grief, I was blocking the energy around my pelvic area with a kind of energetic stop. Although energy work per se is not part of a Mother-Baby Bonding Session, taking time to do such a session allowed me to see what I was doing with my field—and thus shift it.

If you are not sure whether you want to keep a child or not, it can be very helpful to talk with the child. Remember that the baby at this point has a different vantage point than a person with a developed ego. A baby in the womb still has a broad view of the universe, and a perspective that might be very helpful to you.

If you know for sure that you want to end a pregnancy, it can also be helpful to talk with the baby. You might say, "Why? Why would you want to connect with this being if you are not going to keep it?" You would be surprised. Many mothers could avoid a lot of guilt and grief about ending a pregnancy by listening to the wise words of their children and by hearing the baby's perspective. It may not be an easy thing to do, but to have a conversation with the baby *before* an abortion, to explain what you are doing and why, and to receive that child's understanding and acceptance—what a powerful experience!

You may find that the baby knew all along that this was going to happen. Or not. You may find a being ready to be born and very disappointed. In that case, here is your chance to explain why you don't feel ready—or perhaps talk about a time in the future when you might feel more ready.

If you are planning to birth the child, and then allow another family who is more prepared for a child to adopt this baby, here is your chance to explain that in advance and prepare the baby, so the transition for the baby—and for you—is smoother and easier.

We all need closure in our relationships. A conversation with a child that you are not planning to keep, for whatever reason, can give both you and the child this closure.

For any parent who loses a child before birth, whether from stillbirth, miscarriage or the decision to end a pregnancy for any reason, it may be helpful to create your own ceremony to mark the end of this being's brief life. One of my friends well-versed in Native American ceremonies sat on a rock while she was miscarrying. She buried what passed out of her and said a ceremony over it. Whatever your religion or belief system, you can make your own ceremony to mark the passing of this soul. You may want to talk to the baby about what kind of ceremony to do and how she would like to participate in that ceremony in the following exercises.

⸰❧⸰

Exercises During and Following a Miscarriage

When I say "during" a miscarriage, I don't necessarily mean the two-hour or so period of time when the principal part of the miscarriage is occurring, although you could try this if you wanted to. Usually there is bleeding before and after this main part of the miscarriage and you may know weeks before the main event that you are in the process of miscarrying.

I hope you did not begin this book with the exercises to conceive a child and are now facing a miscarriage, but, as common as miscarriages are, I am sure this will happen to more than one person who reads this book. If this is the case, I just want you to know my heart goes out to you. You will be all too familiar with these exercises, and may not need any guidance at all to connect to your baby.

If you are trying to conceive a baby or already pregnant, but miscarried in the past, you may want to try the second exercise to bring completion to the miscarriage.

As always, find a comfortable place to sit, with your feet on the ground, in a place where you can be quiet and undisturbed.

1.   Do a short grounding exercise as explained in Chapter One.

2.   Once you feel grounded and relaxed, place your hands on your belly and take a few deep breaths.

3.   Imagine that your hands are sinking into your belly and actually going into your womb and holding your baby.

4.   If you know, or fear, you may be miscarrying, you may feel a lot of emotion at this point. Just let yourself feel the emotions. Let yourself cry, if you need to. Don't hold back your emotions, or try to talk yourself out of them. Let yourself be wherever you are.

5.   Take a moment to feel into your baby and feel his energy.

6.   Open your heart and say whatever you need to say

to your baby.

7.   As always, listen/sense/tune into a response in whatever way you do that.

8.   Although you are losing the physical child, you can and will stay connected to the energetic child you conceived. So while it may be helpful to say good-bye, you can also be aware of your continuing energetic connection to this baby. Take a moment now to feel into that connection. If you wish, you can ask the baby about that connection and how it works.

9.   If you want to, you can also ask the baby whether she plans to stay around if you try to get pregnant again, or if she will be moving on to other experiences now.

10. If you feel like this soul will be moving on, you may want to ask why the baby chose to have this brief experience with the physical and see what response you get.

11. Whether you hear words, or receive vague sensations, open yourself up to anything your baby may want to communicate to you.

12. Say a tender farewell and send all your love to your baby.

If you have made a decision that you cannot keep a child you are carrying, you may want to do a version of the exercise above to explain your decision to that child and have a completing conversation with that child.

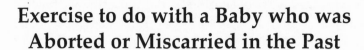

Exercise to do with a Baby who was Aborted or Miscarried in the Past

1.   Sit comfortably with both feet on the ground. Take a few deep breaths, and ground your feet into the ground. Imagine those lines of light going from your feet down through the floor, through the foundation of the house, into the soil, through the bedrock, and deep into the earth, where they connect with the iron and nickel core of the earth.

2.   Feel and breathe your connection to the earth. Feel your energy dropping down into your feet and the softness of the earth holding you. Let go of any stress or tension you feel in your body.

3.   Take a few deep breaths and set your intent to connect with this baby from the past. Let yourself feel in your heart your connection to that baby. Sense into the room around you and see if you feel the presence of that baby anywhere in the room.

4.   If you feel a presence, take some time to just sense into that presence. How does it feel? What is the quality of its energy? Is it soft? Energetic?

5.   Let yourself feel any emotions you may feel about connecting to this baby. You may feel joy at the reconnection. You may feel sadness and need to cry. Let whatever happens for you just happen.

6.   Send a message to this being. What do you want to say? Open your heart and say whatever it is you would like to say to this being.

7.   Listen/sense for a response. It may be a response in words, or it may be a very subtle energy. Remember

that even if you don't hear a response in words, there are many other ways of sensing/communicating with your baby.

8.   You may have questions for your baby. Some women who are still planning to conceive may want to ask if this soul plans to try to come again. You may also find that the soul you are connecting with is a soul you already know in one of your living children. Or you may plan never to have a child. Whatever your case, continue conversing with this being until you have said everything you want to say and feel complete.

9.   Remember that even if you don't feel any response at all coming from this being, she can still hear you and your intent.

10. When you are finished, take time to make a complete farewell with this being. Honor your connection to this soul, and your courage to go into these feelings from the past to make this connection and bring completion for yourself and this being.

Chapter Eleven

CONVERSATIONS
DURING BIRTH

*I*n Chapter Four, I described how I received my son's name while I was in the Monroe Institute's week-long introductory program, Gateway. One of the exercises was to go to different levels of consciousness and ask the same question at those different levels, and see what different answers we got. I decided to ask what would make my labor and delivery easier. One of the answers I received was "Call the baby by his name." I saw myself standing, in the last pushing stage of labor, calling, "Jacob, Jacob, Jacob!"

What will your relationship and communication be with your baby *during* birth? This huge transition for him and for you—could you keep a communication going during this process? How would that facilitate the birth? I honestly don't know the answer to these questions. I did not follow the advice to call my baby by his name during birth, nor did I try to keep communicating with him. I actually did not think about the possibility until much later.

However, I did not have this book to read before my delivery. Nor had I read Rosalind McKnight's book, published just the year before, in which she reports her experiences with Robert Monroe working on different levels of consciousness. McKnight was the initial tester of many Monroe Institute techniques. During one session she describes the process of birth in the year 3000.

"People are born in the same manner, but again, the process is much more highly evolved," she reports. "There is complete communication with the embryo from the time of conception. Schooling begins at the moment of conception. Therefore, the birth process is much simpler—because the child takes more responsibility for its entry into the physical plane.

"The child has a complete understanding of what is happening in birth. There is pure and absolute communication on the mental level. There is no pain or difficulty for the mother. The whole process of birth has evolved. Even hospitals are different, and there are no hospitals as we know them today."[1]

McKnight's description matches what I envision and hope for the future of childbirth. That future begins now—with you! The exercises at the end of this chapter are designed for you to do during birth. I would suggest you read them and become familiar with them before your delivery. If you want to, ask your partner to use the book to guide you through the exercises.

While I did not heed the advice to call my child by his name during childbirth, I did follow another piece of advice I received during that session—and it was a crucial part of my delivery. The Monroe Institute's *Opening the Way* series for birth and delivery had a huge impact on my son's birth.

Like my mother, I went to labor in the evening. I was just lying down to go to bed about 9 o'clock, when my water broke. I stayed at home and managed to sleep a few hours during the night, and went into the birth center the next morning. My labor was going well, but around midday I

---

[1]McKnight, Rosalind, *Cosmic Journeys: My Out-of-Body Explorations with Robert A. Monroe* (Hampton Roads Publishing Co., 1999), p. 285.

began to experience back labor. It felt to me as though my body was avoiding the pain and true work by displacing the pain into my back. It did not feel as though the birth was advancing very well.

Then I remembered that I had brought *Opening the Way* and a headset. I put the headset on and started the tape for labor and delivery. Immediately my pain and my labor came back to the front of my body. My back stopped hurting. The muscles around my womb started working more intensely than ever. I could actually feel my cervix working. The pain was more intense, but it bothered me less. It was as through I had a container to hold the pain and the labor.

I was so stunned by this marked difference in my body that I took the headset off again. The difference was real. Every time I took the headset off, the pain went back into my back, and the labor slowed down. Every time I put the headset back on, the pain came round to the front, and my muscles began working more efficiently. How I wished I had started using the tapes earlier!

My son was born at 7:32 p.m. My mother, who started labor at the same time I did, delivered her first baby at 2 a.m. the following night. *Opening the Way* possibly cut about seven hours off my labor.

I have talked with several other women who used *Opening the Way* during their delivery and they all say the same thing. No one can know for certain, of course, because we can't run the same delivery twice, with and without *Opening the Way*. But they all felt that *Opening the Way* had made their delivery significantly shorter and smoother.[2] *Opening the Way* works so well for birth and delivery because it produces

---

[2] In case you were wondering, I have no official relationship with the Monroe Institute, other than being an alumna of Gateway, and receive no compensation for promoting their products. I simply found *Opening the Way* so helpful that I want to share it with as many people as possible.

a configuration of brain waves that promotes surrender to the natural process taking place in your body. My guess is that this same configuration of brain waves could promote communication with your baby. Of course, you may find your labor is too intense to try talking to your baby. You may be too focused on the process.

But wouldn't it be wonderful if, between contractions, you could connect with your baby, see how she is doing, reassure her, share how it is with you. Imagine doing this journey together consciously, each of you sharing your thoughts, fears, excitement. How different this would make the experience for you and for your baby!

Could you keep this connection even during contractions? If you try—if you try anything in the book, but especially this birth connection—please contact me and let me know how it went!

No matter how your labor goes, this continuing connection between you and your baby can be helpful. If you and your doctor or midwife decide you need a C-section, you can let your baby know about that decision and, in the few minutes you may have, prep him for that different kind of transition.

My hope is that you would also know, because you are talking with your baby—or at least have a sense—whether the baby was in distress during the birth process. But I would definitely not hold yourself responsible for this kind of specific information. That would an amazing bonus, if you could know about any problems from the baby. The most important thing is to keep a loving connection and an open receptivity to your baby during the birth process.

❦

Exercises for Labor and Delivery

Every woman is different and every woman's experience during childbirth is different. Exactly what you will need and what will help you during your labor and delivery will be unique. The exercises below are general guidelines. Using what you know about connecting to your baby from your practice during pregnancy, you can tailor the exercises to meet whatever you and your baby need during this delivery.

The main point of these exercises is that you keep an open line of communication with your baby and make this transition as easy as possible for you and your baby.

I received another piece of guidance at the Monroe Institute that was key to my delivery and which forms the basis of an exercise below. When I asked how to make my labor and delivery easier, I was told to "be one with the pain." I didn't know how important that advice would be until I was deep in labor.

I found that if I resisted the contraction at all or tried to rise about the pain, or even thought about something else, I had a very hard time. But I became very quiet and focused and completely surrendered to each contraction, if I really tried to "be one with the pain," then my body could handle anything that came along.

This took focus and quiet. I might have had a more difficult time had I been in a hospital, with more people coming and going, than in the birth center where my son was born. But wherever you are—in a hospital, in a birth center, at home— this technique, which is spelled out below, may be helpful to you.

Before we begin the exercise, I want to share some important advice that I received from experienced mothers before my son's birth:

1. **Keep breathing**. Breathing is the key to relaxing, to keep blood and oxygen flowing, to keep yourself grounded and as comfortable as possible. Obviously, you will never stop breathing completely, but many of us have a tendency to hold our breath when we are facing something challenging. Remember to breathe as much and as fully as you can. This will help you and your baby.

2. **Drink lots of water early in your labor**. I cannot emphasize this enough. There may come a time in your labor when you find you cannot drink or eat anymore. If you have a short labor, this won't matter very much. But if you have a long labor, then drinking as much as you can early in the labor will be very important. If you are hungry in the beginning of labor and can eat, then do that too—you may need the nourishment.

3. **If your labor starts in the evening, or continues through a night, try to sleep during the night**, even if only for a few hours. This can make a huge difference later to your fatigue level and consequently how well you feel both during your labor and once your baby is born. If you have trouble sleeping, you can use *Opening the Way* or the *Catnapper Album* to help you relax and go to sleep.

If you are planning to have someone read this exercise to you during the birth, don't forget to take the book, as well as the *Opening the Way* series and a headset if you are planning to use them.

Exercise Between Contractions

1.   When you are sure your labor has truly begun, breathe, feel yourself in your feet and connected to the earth, and connect with your baby in the way that you have practiced during your pregnancy.

2.   Let your baby know that the journey out of the womb has begun. (He may already know this, but your confirmation will be helpful.)

3.   Acknowledge your feelings to yourself and to your baby—excitement, nervousness, happiness—whatever those feelings are. *"I am feeling excited and a little nervous. I can't wait to see you."*

4.   Ask the baby how he is doing. How is he feeling—emotionally and physically? Is there anything he needs from you? Feel/listen for a response. If you feel he needs something from you, try to provide it.

5.   Remind the baby that, as you prepped him, he may feel some squeezing on his body. Assure him this is normal and necessary and will not last. Let him know he will continue to stay connected to you through the umbilical cord and it will provide all his oxygen and nourishment throughout the process.

6.   Encourage the baby to relax during the contractions and totally surrender to what is happening. Let him know the more he and you surrender and relax, the quicker and more easily the process will go.

7.   Try to let him know what is happening:

"I am going to try to sleep some now..."

"We are going to stay home for a while and let the

contractions progress..."

"We are going to the hospital/birth center in a few minutes..."

"We are checking into the hospital now. They are going to get us a nice room where you can be born peacefully."

If you are doing a home birth: *"The midwife is on the way..."*

8. Remind your baby when he comes out of your body, he may feel a little cold, but everyone will do everything they can to make sure he feels warm again. If he is going to get a bath at birth, or just wiped off, let him know that. Also remind him he will need to start breathing on his own.

9. If you are doing a water birth, remind him he will come out into warm water, and he can start breathing once his head is out of the water.

10. Let him know you will be with him and close to him at all times.

11. Naturally, if any complications develop during your labor and delivery, or any special procedures need to be done, part of the process will be connecting with your baby and explaining what is going on.

12. Let him know that, if for any reason he has to be separated from you for a procedure, his father or your partner will stay with him (if you have arranged this with your medical provider, which I hope you have).

Don't forget that the process of labor and delivery can be intense and what you may be able to pick up from your baby may be heightened, or may be greatly diminished.

⋘⋙

Exercise During Contractions

1. When you feel a contraction starting, let yourself relax and totally be one with the contraction. That means totally focusing on what's happening in your body, mentally and emotionally, and totally surrendering to it. Let your body relax completely and go with whatever is happening. For me, it helped to say to myself, "Be one with the pain." (Not all women experience pain during childbirth—if you don't, good for you.)

2. If you are using *Opening the Way*, don't forget to start using it early in the process. The earlier you start using it, the more it can help you.

Chapter Twelve

COMMUNICATING WITH A NEWBORN: PREPARING FOR YOUR BABY'S FIRST FEW MOMENTS OF LIFE

When your baby arrives, hold him in your arms. Gaze at him. Here is your baby, the one you have been communicating with. What is he saying? Can you still hear his words or feel his energy?

Those first few minutes after birth are precious ones. They are important moments for you and your baby to form a new kind of connection. For the first time you can see and touch your baby. If you have been communicating regularly with your baby before birth, then this bonding at birth will be a continuation of a process you started many months before. Even now, the skills you have learned to use before birth may serve you well.

For many years newborns were—and often still are—treated as though they were not intelligent and that their cries and smiles have no meaning. But recent research shows that not only are newborns intelligent, but they have an understanding of themselves, their surroundings and other people far beyond what we realize.

David Chamberlain, a psychologist and former president of the Association for Pre- and Perinatal Psychology and Health, hypnotized young people aged nine to 23 and asked them about their births. In his book, *The Mind of Your Newborn Baby*, he chronicles how these babies were completely aware of their surroundings, "[d]isplaying a wisdom for which we are in no way prepared."[1]

His subjects report understanding complex family dynamics and how those dynamics affected them. They were often dismayed and angry at how they were treated at birth. They remember being turned upside down and hit, being cold, being handled roughly, not being given to their mothers to hold. They talk about their sadness at thoughtless random comments made about them as if they were not there. They report the discomfort of eye drops and the pain of injections.

Repeatedly, the young people in Chamberlain's study talk about how they tried to communicate at birth, but no one noticed.

"They seemed to ignore me," remembered one girl. "They were doing things *to* me—to the *outside* of me. But they acted like that's all there was. When I tried to tell them things, they just wouldn't listen, like that noise wasn't really anything. It didn't sound too impressive, but it was all I had." Based on the "crazy" way the doctor and nurses were treating her and how little they seemed to know what she needed, she concluded. "I just really felt like I was more intelligent than they were."[2]

One baby knew that her mother was hemorrhaging and felt her own body was the only thing keeping her mother from bleeding to death. She faced an agonizing decision: Did she allow herself to be born, knowing her mother might die? Or did she stay in the birth canal, even though she herself might die?

---

[1] Chamberlain, David, *The Mind of Your Newborn Baby* (North Atlantic Books, 1998), p. 158.

[2] Ibid p.157.

"There's too much blood all over. Nobody knows it yet. She is completely filled with it, and I'm the only one keeping it from coming out!

"Ohhh......If I come out and she dies, she'll never know how much I love her! I want to know her. She talked to me a lot before I was born, but nobody else knew because they'd think she was silly."[3]

I find this quote very interesting, not only because it shows how a newborn understands issues of life and death (Both mother and baby were fine, in the end.), but also because it tells us about her love for and her connection with her mother. It demonstrates how she appreciated her mother's attempts to talk with her. She even knew that her mother hid these attempts because she was afraid people would think they were "silly."

How different your baby's experience has been! Not only do you talk to your baby, but you know enough to listen for a response. I hope you will not hide these attempts because you think people find them "silly," although you may not talk to everyone about them, simply because they are so tender and private. But remember, every time you share your experiences of communication with your baby with another woman, you become a kind of ambassador, changing the way we think about babies. By sharing your conversations with your little one, you may help other women connect with their own babies.

At birth you have the chance to see and touch your baby with your hands for the first time. That experience is so rich and full—simply to be with your baby is enough. But, if you are not too tired from a long labor and delivery, you can also use the skills you have developed during pregnancy to continue to connect with your baby, and receive answers from her about how she is doing in this new environment.

As much as you can, set an atmosphere for those first few

[3] Ibid, p. 159.

minutes and hours that facilitates your baby's transitions and the connection between the two of you. If you give birth in your own home or a birth center, it will probably be easy to make sure the atmosphere is calm and welcoming. If you give birth in a hospital, as most women do, you need to find out what the procedures of the hospital are at birth, and make sure you have communicated clearly to the hospital what you want—before your delivery. Many parents do not realize that standard hospital procedures are not required. You have choices. You have important decisions to make about your baby's first few moments outside the womb that will affect her for the rest of his life.

The most important thing of all: Make sure the baby stays with you and does not sleep in a nursery. There is no good reason for a healthy baby to be away from her mother at all at birth, or in the first few days of life.

If the baby has problems at birth, she actually needs her mother and father's love and attention even more. If a baby needs to leave her mother's side for special procedures, many hospitals will allow the father to go with the baby and stay near her.

Most hospitals put prophylactic eye drops in the newborn baby's eyes to guard against bacteria from chlamydia, syphilis, or gonorrhea which, if present in the birth canal, can cause blindness in babies. Growing numbers of parents are opting not to administer these eye drops to their babies. Even though these eye drops are often required by law, you have a choice to ask them not to be administered. Unless you know that you have been exposed to chlamydia, syphilis, or gonorrhea, you may want to inform your doctor and the hospital, verbally and in writing, that you do not want your baby to receive these drops. The drops keep the baby from seeing clearly. The eye-to-eye contact between mother and child—and father and child—is a key part of this crucial bonding time. During these first few moments of life, the baby needs to be able to see you and her surroundings clearly.

Since 1991 babies have been routinely vaccinated at birth in hospitals for hepatitis B. Hepatitis B is transmitted through blood, sexual contact, or sharing needles, much like AIDS. It is a disease contracted in adolescence or adulthood. Babies are only at risk to contract Hepatitis B if their mother or another close family member has the disease.[4]

There has been much debate in the medical community about the wisdom of this practice, since children are not usually at risk for the disease, although it does protect young children who are subject to sexual abuse. Many physicians have not only pointed out the absurdity of vaccinating infants for an adult disease, but argued against the enormous expense of routinely vaccinating all babies at birth.[5]

Receiving a vaccine at birth is, I believe, a completely unnecessarily traumatic experience. These are your child's first few moments of experience of life outside the womb. They should be as comfortable and easy and stress-free as possible. Lights should be low, the people present should be calm and welcoming, and any uncomfortable medical procedures that are not absolutely necessary for the immediate health and safety of the baby and mother should be avoided. Clearly a vaccination for hepatitis B does not fall into the category of necessary for the immediate health and safety of the baby, unless the mother carries the disease.

Babies are also routinely subjected to a blood test, usually by a prick to the heel, for a battery for possible syndromes. You can choose, however, not to have this procedure done at birth, but five days after birth, with your regular pediatrician or your midwife. If you choose to do it at the hospital, make sure that it is done at least the day after birth and that you are with your baby, preferably with the baby in your arms when it is done.

---

[4] Neustaeder, Randall, *The Vaccine Guide* (North Atlantic Books, 1996), p. 174.
[5] Ibid, p. 173.

If you have a baby boy, you will have to decide whether or not to circumcise your baby. A growing number of people are choosing not to circumcise their baby boys. This of course is a very personal decision. I would just urge you to think about your baby boy and how much what happens to him in his first days of life will affect him for the rest of his life. Many baby boys are circumcised at a day or two old with no anesthesia. Think about this for a minute. This is an operation. The doctor is cutting your child's skin in the most sensitive part of his body. If a doctor tells you, it's okay, it doesn't hurt the baby, don't believe it. Babies are not less sensitive than adults. They are hundreds of times more sensitive.

I personally believe that, unless you have a religious reason, this operation is completely unnecessary. I believe human beings have been designed the way they are for a reason. That fold of skin is there to protect the baby's delicate penis. Yes, it can get dirty under there, but it's not hard to clean it, or to teach a child to clean under it properly.

Surgery is a traumatic and invasive experience to the human system, even if you are old enough to understand why it's happening and that it will save your life. Your baby is just learning about the world and what life is like outside the womb. Let him come into the world softly and easily, not painfully.

If you feel you must circumcise your baby, at least don't have it done at birth. Have it done a few days or a few weeks after birth. Make sure that doctor or hospital uses anesthesia. Make sure you are present and can surround the baby with your love and your energy field during the operation.

In the Jewish tradition the baby is circumcised at 10 days. A religious ceremony accompanies the circumcision. A rabbi leads the ceremony and holds the space. The parents and often grandparents are an integral part of the ceremony, holding a container for their child and comforting the baby after the surgery. I feel sure this gives the baby a very different experience than the medical atmosphere of a hospital with no family present.

What does your baby think of all these procedures? Take some time to find out from your baby in this first exercise. The second exercise is for you to continue dialoguing with your baby *after* birth.

∞

Exercise to Ask Your Baby About Procedures at Birth

1.   Ground in whatever way works best for you, and send your energy deep into the earth. Rest quietly, letting the earth support you for a few minutes.

2.   Placing your hands on your belly, let yourself connect with your baby. As usual, greet your baby, let yourself say whatever comes to your heart and mind to say, and sense into your baby's response.

3.   As always, ask if the baby has anything to communicate to you, and just be open to the response.

4.   Let your baby know you would like to have a conversation about her first few minutes after birth. Tell her what you expect this time will be like—remind her where you will be, who will be there, how happy you will be to see her and hold her in your arms. Spend some time dreaming with your baby about how special this time will be.

5.   Then, ask about any procedures that you are wondering about—vaccinations, eye drops, heel prick, circumcision if it's a boy, etc. This is a good time to use yes/no questions as to whether or not the baby feels these procedures are a good idea. Then you can try to get

a more detailed response.

6.　If you already know what you want for your baby, you may not feel the need to ask about all of these procedures. In that case, you may want to explain to the baby what's going to happen—which procedures are going to occur, how, and why.

7.　Before you close the conversation with your baby, you may want to tell the baby once again how excited and happy you are about the prospect of her birth, and how much you are looking forward to seeing her.

8.　When you are finished talking with your baby, bring the conversation to closure with an assurance of your love and a gentle farewell.

⟨✪⟩

Exercise to Connect to Your Baby After Birth

1.　The experience of holding your baby and seeing her at birth is such an amazing experience that you probably will not need any more than that. You may also be too tired or overwhelmed to think about doing an exercise like this. But you may find that tuning into the baby in this way right after birth makes a difference to your connection with the baby. Don't hesitate to do this exercise in whatever variation works for you. It may be just a quick check-in with your baby.

2.　If you are not too tired, just do a quick grounding— send your energy down to your feet, and let yourself get calm and relaxed.

3.　You may try this exercise different ways. You may want to try it gazing into your baby's eyes. You may want to try it while your baby is nursing for the first

time, or while she is sleeping afterwards. See what works
for you.

4.   Whichever way you are trying, let yourself connect
with your baby through your heart the same way you
did before she was born. Say any words to her that
come to your mind—how happy you are to see her, how
beautiful she is, whatever your heart wants to say.

5.   Sense/listen for a response. I don't know if this will
be easier or harder to do while looking at your baby. Let
me know!

6.   Ask any questions you may have to ask your baby.
Don't forget to ask if your baby has anything to say to
you.

7.   As always, close the conversation in a loving way.

Once again, I am very curious about your experiences
during this time. If you try any version of this exercise after
birth, please email me at penny@motherbabytalk.com and
let me know what you experienced. And enjoy this precious
time with your baby!

Chapter Thirteen
TALKING WITH YOUR NEW BABY

*L*ike light falling from a star, your little one has fallen from the sky to come to you. What do I mean by this? I mean that your precious baby has incarnated through you, through your light, through your cells, into a new being—a new physical being, for his true being may be very old indeed. What kind of steward will you be of this new being? Only time will tell. But one thing is sure: You were chosen by your baby to provide exactly the kind of environment he needs to set him on his path—whatever that path may be.

It may be confusing—and certainly tiring—for you these first few month and years of his life. What exactly does he need? What is he trying to tell you when he cries?

I remember when my baby was five days old. Usually he nursed in the night and then went right back to sleep. But that night was different. He fussed, he cried. Hours later, he was still awake. Finally, my husband got up to see what was happening. "He won't sleep!" I cried, exhausted. My husband took one look at him and said, "He's cold. Put some more clothes on him."

I felt like an idiot. Somehow I had not computed this in my brain. My husband got socks and put them on the baby's feet. He put more clothes on him and we covered him up warmly. He fell asleep instantly.

There may be many times where physical clues—cries, looks, eye contact—may fail you. Until your baby learns to talk, he must use nonverbal clues to talk with you. Unless you can connect with him in other ways!

I did not continue to use my skills to connect to my son and find out what he needed once my baby was born. But I wish I had. He, fortunately, is such a good communicator, with and without words, that usually I knew what he needed. But I encourage you to try. In some ways, it is easier to tune into a baby you cannot see or touch, because those nonphysical senses are all you have. But the process of reaching out to your baby's larger self through your cord connections is no different when the baby is in your arms than when he was in the womb. It's only a question of where our attention goes.

I did—and do—continue to connect to that large being which seemed to be my son's true being, and which I now call his guide. That being is still as filled with love for me as ever. I go to this being whenever I have questions about raising my son that I cannot answer. Which school should he go to? Is this summer camp a good idea for him?

I don't connect with this guide very often anymore, because my son talks now. Now he can tell me himself what he wants and needs. And he is quite vocal about it.

Sometimes I wonder if his ability to communicate so clearly was affected by the fact that we began communicating before he came out of the womb. Those early opportunities to converse, my willingness to listen to both words and nonverbal clues such as repeated kicks—did these experiences strengthen the centers of communication in his brain? Did they open better pathways for his expectations about and abilities to communicate? Certainly he protests loudly if I am not giving him my full attention during our conversations. "Mommy, you're not *really* listening!" he says.

This book has been about listening—*really* listening to your baby. I hope these conversations have helped you form a closer bond with your baby and allowed you to get to know him better—even before he arrives. If you want to, you can continue tuning into your baby the same way now that he is here—and continue getting to know him better—with or without physical words and conversations. You can continue to have your own special conversation with your growing baby, even while you hold him in your arms.

❦

Exercise to Connect with Your Baby After Birth

Remembering what it was like to have an infant, I think just the act of sitting down, being still and getting grounded will be a nice experience for you, and helpful to your baby while he is learning about grounding into a physical body. If you are really tired, sitting down and grounding may actually put you to sleep. That's fine—if that's what you needed, then that's perfect.

After you have tried this exercise a few times, you may find that you can just "tune in" to your baby and communicate on this level at any time. Wouldn't it be nice if you could use these skills to find out why your baby is crying on those days when you have no idea?

Of course, you also have all your skills of reading your baby's verbal and nonverbal cues, and some families use signs once the baby is old enough to do that. My son made up his own signs and signals. When he wanted to go outside, he would look at me and take a deep breath through his nose, as if smelling the fresh air.

But if I had thought of it, and had owned a book such as this to support me, I would have tried to connect with my baby this way, to have a better idea of what he wanted and needed.

1.   You may do this exercise holding your baby, while your baby is asleep, or any other time your baby does not need you. I don't know if you could also do this while nursing your baby, if you are breastfeeding, or whether that would be distracting. Try it and see!

2.   Relax in a chair, feet on the ground and let your body relax in the chair. Let your feet sink into ground. Imagine them sinking through the floor, through the foundation of the house, into the soil and deep into the earth. See if you can feel the bones of the earth—the rocks—through your feet. Connect with the deep, molten rock part of the earth, and let that heat come into your body.

3.   Finally, connect solidly with the nickel-iron core of the earth. Just for a moment, imagine you are in the center of the earth, being held gently by the earth. Feel how the earth knows you—knows you as an individual—and fulfills all of your needs.

4.   Let that earth energy come up through your feet, through your legs, through your pelvis and your stomach and into your heart. Now imagine you are sending a line of light from your heart, up through your chest, neck and head, and out the top of your head. Connect to spirit/sky energy.

5.   Open your crown chakra in the top of your head: just imagine that it is full and spinning. Do the same with your sixth chakra, the third-eye chakra, in the front and back of your head; the throat chakra, front and back, and your heart chakra. Finally, return to your grounding and make sure your first chakra is open and spinning. Don't worry if you don't really feel any of this happening— just imagine it is happening and set your intent for your chakras to be open. That is enough.

6.   Feel free to do an abbreviated version of any of this, depending on how much time you have. Don't skip the grounding, but do as much of the chakra spinning as you

have time and energy.

7.   Now let your heart open and connect with your baby, wherever he is—in bed, in your arms, on the couch, playing on the floor. Feel the heart cord connection between you and your baby.

8.   As always, greet him and send him your love energetically. Do you get an energetic, vibrational response? You may want to try this exercise not holding your baby, and you may want to try it gazing into his eyes, whichever works better for you to focus on the energetic connection.

9.   Tell your baby anything that is on your mind or in your heart to tell him. Listen/sense for a response.

10. Ask him if he has anything to share with you. Listen/sense for the answer.

11. If you have specific questions or concerns for your baby, now is the time to ask. Try journaling the answers, or ask yes/no questions if that is the best way you can feel a response. There are so many questions you could ask an infant—about sleeping arrangements, about how to help your baby sleep through the night, about the way he wants to be fed, about whether he is teething, the list is endless.

12. As always, when you are finished, be sure to close the session with him.

I am curious whether this exercise is helpful—or possible— for busy new mothers. Please, if you try this exercise—or any of the others in the book—contact me at penny@ motherbabytalk.com and tell me about your experiences. You may also contact me if you wish to make an appointment for a guided Mother-Baby Bonding Session.

Good luck! And congratulations! What a beautiful baby!

About the Author

Penny D. Chang is an energy healer practicing in Charlottesville, Virginia, with local clients in Virginia and distance clients in the U.S., Europe and Australia. She graduated from Bryn Mawr College magna cum laude with honors in history in 1985 and from the Barbara Brennan School of Healing as a Brennan Healing Science Practitioner in 2001. Upon graduation Chang and her husband founded the Healing Heart Space in downtown Charlottesville, where they teach energy healing skills, and Chang offers private sessions in energy healing, Healing Movement and Mother-Baby Bonding Before Birth. Chang is also a dancer and choreographer of modern dance and dance improvisation. In 2012 she became a Certified Movement Analyst (CMA) through the Laban/Bartenieff Institute of Movement Studies Modular Program at the University of Maryland.

Parents who would like to share their experiences of dialoging with their children during pregnancy or before conception, or who would like support for those dialogues through private sessions, are encouraged to contact her at www.motherbabytalk.com.

6309670R00081

Printed in Great Britain
by Amazon.co.uk, Ltd.,
Marston Gate.